2.25

THE
PHYSICAL DIMENSIONS
OF
CONSCIOUSNESS

THE CENTURY
PSYCHOLOGY SERIES

EDITED BY

RICHARD M. ELLIOTT, PH.D., *University of Minnesota*

---

*EXPERIMENTAL CHILD STUDY, by Florence L. Goodenough and John E. Anderson; *HUMAN LEARNING, by Edward L. Thorndike; *HISTORY OF EXPERIMENTAL PSYCHOLOGY, by Edwin G. Boring; *EFFECTIVE STUDY HABITS, by Charles Bird; *GREAT EXPERIMENTS IN PSYCHOLOGY, by Henry E. Garrett; *PHYSIQUE AND INTELLECT, by Donald G. Paterson; *PURPOSIVE BEHAVIOR IN ANIMALS AND MEN, by Edward C. Tolman; *ASSOCIATION THEORY TO-DAY, by Edward S. Robinson; *DIAGNOSING PERSONALITY AND CONDUCT, by P. M. Symonds; *THE WILD BOY OF AVEYRON, by Jean-Marc-Gaspard Itard, translated by George and Muriel Humphrey; *THE PHYSICAL DIMENSIONS OF CONSCIOUSNESS, by Edwin G. Boring; *SEVEN PSYCHOLOGIES, by Edna Heidbreder; SOCIAL PSYCHOLOGY, by Charles Bird; BEAUTY AND HUMAN NATURE, by Albert R. Chandler; HUMAN MOTIVES AND INCENTIVES, by H. A. Toops; SUGGESTION AND HYPNOSIS, by Clark L. Hull; CHILD PSYCHOLOGY, by John E. Anderson; DEVELOPMENTAL PSYCHOLOGY, by Florence L. Goodenough.

OTHER VOLUMES TO BE ARRANGED

* Published

As of April, 1933

The Century Psychology Series
Richard M. Elliott, Editor

THE PHYSICAL DIMENSIONS OF CONSCIOUSNESS

BY EDWIN G. BORING

PROFESSOR OF PSYCHOLOGY IN
HARVARD UNIVERSITY

THE CENTURY CO.
NEW YORK : LONDON

PREFACE

In both physiology and psychology there is a strong and healthy tradition against what is called 'speculation.' Experimentalism is not yet so firmly established in either of these new sciences that it does not need a fully conscious, and at times slightly vehement, support; and naïve epistemology holds that science espouses observation and rejects speculation. Nevertheless, I am convinced that careful consideration does not support a strict opposition between observation and speculation. At least every observation is also essentially an interpretation, a view fundamental to the relational theory of consciousness which this book propounds. Actually this whole matter can be regarded as a question of the use of hypothesis in science, and it seems to me that there cannot be any longer a doubt that profitable observation must be predetermined, as to the nature of the correlation which it seeks to establish, by hypothesis. The valid dichotomy lies between useful hypothesis and dangerous speculation, and here the line of demarcation is necessarily indeterminate and personal. The reader will have no difficulty in discovering that I look upon the contents of this book as 'useful hypothesis,' but perhaps he needs to be told that I shall not be disappointed if there are those who contemn this text as 'dangerous speculation.' Neither physiology nor psychology is yet ready to do without its cautious conservatives.

However, the 'speculation' in this book is for the most part not mine but every one's. My general purpose in the treatment of physiological hypotheses has been to render explicit the assumptions that underlie the accepted psycho-physiological thinking of to-day. I have tried to make explicit what is usually only implicit, and to follow such explicated implications along to their natural consequences wherever any profit seemed ready to accrue. I hope that radicals will approve my courage, but I feel that conservatives should also be glad to have discovered to them the insecure timbers in their own house.

Perhaps the fundamental problem of hypothesis arises in connection with the principle of psychophysiological correlation, that the data of consciousness, as introspection yields them, imply the occurrence of physiological processes that cause, or parallel, or are identical with the conscious events. This is the basic psychophysiological hypothesis and most psychological facts and theories presuppose such a correlation. Because he accepts this assumption, the psychologist believes, as a rule, that a psychological theory is most firmly established when it can be provided with an explicit physiological foundation, and physiologists also prefer to have their psychological theories grounded in physiology. I confess that it seems to me to be a comment upon the vanity of physiologists and the modesty of psychologists that it is only recently that we have begun to hear the suggestion that this important hypothesis is reversible, that a physiological theory of neural action ought not seriously to be maintained if it is incompatible with psychological fact, and that psychology stands just as ready to provide sanctions for neural theory as physiology is prepared to render a symmetrical service to psychology. At any rate I have assumed such a reversible logic, and perhaps my book is partly an example of what happens as a result. That I find myself led to an identity hypothesis of the relation of 'mind' to 'body' is but a detail in contrast with this larger matter.

The doctrine of conscious dimensions, which I believe without proof to be essentially Titchener's way of meeting the challenge of Gestalt psychology and the anti-atomists, seems to me very important and the correct approach to the adequate description of mind. However, I am not willing to stress the doctrine as much as some of its friends would like, because I believe that categories of description, whether they be the psychological dimensions of quality and intensity or the physical dimensions of space, mass, and time, are scientifically arbitrary and temporary, matters of the convenience or economy of description. One does not attempt to discover conscious elements, attributes, or dimensions; one makes them up and uses them as phenomenological exigencies require.

Anyhow, the ideal would be ultimately to get away from conscious dimensions to physical dimensions, to the happy monism of the scientific heaven. Thus it comes about that this book is devoted to the problem of assessing our progress in this direction, and I have therefore called it by what will seem to some a paradoxical title, *The Physical Dimensions of Consciousness*. We are not yet ready to give up the conscious dimensions. We need them now, but I think we are already seeing how it can come about that we shall eventually be able to do without them. I hope—to the dissatisfaction of some of those who have stimulated my thought along these lines—that progress may be rapid in this direction.

My chief intellectual debt in these chapters is undoubtedly to the perpetual colloquium which exists in the Harvard Psychological Laboratory because my colleagues and I cannot avoid argument; and here I think especially of Dr. C. C. Pratt and Dr. J. G. Beebe-Center, because I have been associated with them longest and because they are both irrepressible. However, there are several of us who have argued and differed with enough enthusiasm for us to believe that we must be essentially in agreement. We do not yet know what our common faith is. Perhaps it is in this book; more likely it appears only by implication.

The reader will have no difficulty in discovering the great extent of my debt to Karl S. Lashley. I am impressed by the importance of his research and the experimental work which he has inspired. I am stimulated by his thought. I believe in his outlook upon psychology. I admire his freedom from scholasticism. I like the flavor of his thought. I am inclined to think of the more constructive hypotheses of this book as what Lashley might have said had he been less cautious and conservative. Since he, a radical to some, seems conservative to me, I take this opportunity to apologize to him for the wanton way in which I have used his theories.

The manuscript of these chapters was finished on the evening of March thirty-first last. The next morning I received my copy of the third volume of Troland's *The Principles of Psychophysiology,* the volume on *Cerebration and Action.* Several other scientific papers, relevant to the text, have since appeared, and now I expect at any time a new pronouncement by Nafe on his quantitative theory of feeling. As far as practicable I have added these new references to the notes, while I have been waiting upon certain unavoidable exigencies of publication for the appearance of these chapters. I have read nothing new that would have altered any fundamental exposition, although I might have written differently here and there had I been in possession of these additional materials at the time of composition.

Mr. S. Smith Stevens of the Harvard Laboratory has read this entire manuscript and made valuable suggestions which I have adopted. The editor and Professor Miles A. Tinker at Minnesota have also read in detail and I have profited by their labor. My wife has criticized the manuscript trenchantly and scrutinized the proof meticulously. Dr. William H. Stavsky has drawn many of the figures. Mrs. Frances E. Withington has turned my bad and dangerous typing into good safe copy.

To the following authors and publishers I am grateful for permission to reproduce, sometimes with modification, many of the figures in the text: to Mr. E. D. Adrian and W. W. Norton Company for Figs. 5, 7 and 16; to Professor Alexander Forbes and the Clark University Press for Fig. 6; to Professors E. G. Wever and C. W. Bray and the *Psychological Review* for Figs. 8 and 9; to Professors H. M. Halverson and K. M. Dallenbach for Fig. 11; to Professor K. Koffka and the Clark University Press for Fig. 13; and to Professor K. S. Lashley and the University of Chicago Press for Figs. 14 and 17.

E. G. B.

November 16, 1932
Cambridge, Massachusetts

TABLE OF CONTENTS

CHAPTER   PAGE

1   MIND AND BODY 3

     Dualism 3
     Psychophysical Correlation 8
     Notes 14

2   THE DIMENSIONS OF CONSCIOUSNESS 17

     Sensation and Attributes 17
     The Dimensions of Consciousness 22
     Notes 32

3   INTENSITY 36

     Nerve Excitation 37
     The Multiple Fiber Theory 42
     The Frequency Theory 46
     The Volley Theory 50
     Sensory Intensity 55
     Notes 57

4   EXTENSITY 62

     The Psychological Problem of Space 62
     The Projection Theory 67
     Psychophysiological Correspondence 75
     Extension 78
     The Third Visual Dimension 86
     Size 94
     Form 99
     Localization 107
     Notes 115

Table of Contents

CHAPTER   PAGE

5 TIME 127

    Judgments of Time and Duration 129
    Protensitive Integration 133
    The Physiology of Protensity 137
    Notes 146

6 QUALITY 150

    Modality 151
    Quality within the Modality 158
    Visual Quality 162
    Auditory Quality 165
    Somesthetic Quality 171
    Notes 181

7 THE ORGANIZATION OF CONSCIOUSNESS 187

    Intelligence 188
    Attention 194
    Learning 201
    Notes 212

8 THE NATURE OF CONSCIOUSNESS 221

    The Relational Theory of Consciousness 222
    Relational Physiology 229
    The Dimensions of Consciousness 233
    Notes 236

    INDEX OF NAMES 239

    INDEX OF SUBJECTS 243

THE
PHYSICAL DIMENSIONS
OF
CONSCIOUSNESS

Chapter 1

MIND AND BODY

WHEN Descartes established the scientific dichotomy between mind and body, he provided both the *raison d'être* of modern psychology and the mystery which it has never completely dissolved. Descartes cut the world in two, into mind and matter, just at the time when science was about to begin the course of development which has made it the dominating influence in modern civilization. We all know how successful the physical sciences have been and we can also see that biology has prospered in abandoning a vitalism and identifying itself with the physical side of the Cartesian dichotomy. If Descartes was right, if there are these two worlds, then the success of science in attacking the one forms a challenge for the creation of a science of the other. This view is common in psychology. When psychologists speak of the classification of the sciences they are usually sure of only two sciences —psychology and physics. Yet, if psychology is coördinate with physics and if the scientific method is applicable to both, then it seems strange that psychology has come such a little way when physics has ramified into many fields and has come so far.

Dualism

The Cartesian dichotomy has been impressed upon psychology from the very beginning. It is implicit in British empiricism and associationism. The view that an external

3

world gradually impressed itself upon an inner mind (Locke) is dualistic. Even the view that mind is the only reality (Berkeley) becomes dualistic when it leads to the problem of how a knowledge of an external world comes about. In the nineteenth century the dichotomy between spiritualism and materialism became important and led Fechner to the invention of his psychophysics. Wundt contrasted immediate experience (psychology) with mediate experience (physics). Later introspectionists, like Külpe and Titchener, adopted Avenarius's formula that psychology deals with experience regarded as dependent upon the experiencing individual, while physics deals with independent experience. Psychophysical parallelism has been the usual theory of mind and body, but Descartes's interactionism was just as dualistic. Even the 'double-aspect' theory of mind and body is a dual theory. Behaviorism began, not by identifying consciousness with matter nor by denying consciousness, but by ignoring it as subject-matter for science. There were monistic 'objectivists,' of course, and pluralists, but most psychological thinking for more than two centuries has been referred to a bifocal frame of reference, even when its intent has been to emphasize the one focus and to ignore the other.

The reader must not infer that protests against dualism have not been frequent and loud during the last two decades. The behaviorists have sought to keep to one side of the dichotomy and there to explain everything that used to belong to the other side. There have been monistic systems proposed. Into the evaluation of these views it is not the purpose of the present book to enter. This chapter must serve simply as an elementary introduction to the monistic point of view from which this book is written.

The author believes that neither Wundt's nor Avenarius's formula is satisfactory for a scientific psychology. It was Wundt's view that immediate experience is the subject-matter of psychology. Physics deals with experience mediately. This view leads to the conclusion that psychology deals with "direct experience" (Köhler's term) or with phenomena as such, and makes psychology equivalent to a phenomenology and thus propædeutic to physics, which is mediate to experience because its entities are inferentially derived. If psychology deals with experience and physics is derived from experience, it would seem that physics must be derived from psychology. Such an inversion of historical fact must, however, be unsatisfactory. Hence Külpe and Titchener adhered to Avenarius's view, which, in a sense, reverses the relationship.

Avenarius's position is that there are two ways of regarding experience. Psychology (as Titchener restated Avenarius) regards experience as dependent upon the experiencing individual, whereas physics regards it as independent. Here we seem to have two coördinate points of view and to have avoided the derivation of physics from psychology. However, psychology has now become factually mediate. Experience, instead of being prior to physical entities, like the nervous system, is now held to be dependent upon the experiencing individual; and the experiencing individual is, for all practical intents, the nervous system.

Thus we come out with a circle. Experience is the cognitive ground of those inferences which yield the material of physics (Wundt). The brain is a physical entity. But the brain is actually the essential condition of experience. If conscious phenomena are the materials of experience, then they are both the stuff which yields an object like the brain and also the consequences of the activity of this brain. Psychology, as the science of consciousness, is systematically both prior and posterior to physics. Any such circle must result in epistemological vertigo.

The correct avoidance of this circle, so it seems to the

author, is essentially Külpe's. Historically science is physical science. Psychology, if it is to be a science, must be like physics. Physics deals with very real entities, of which electrons and atoms are typical examples. Such realities exist, but *reality* and *existence* in this sense are the results of inductive inferences accomplished by the experimental method. Thus the events of physics, as Wundt said, are mediate to experience, which stands in the background as the dator of scientific data, unrealizable as reality except inductively.

In the same way psychology must deal with existential reals, which are similarly mediate to experience. There is no way of getting at 'direct experience,' because experience gives itself up to science indirectly, inferentially, by the experimental method. The question as to whether a sensation exists used to mean the question as to whether experience could ever be patterned as a single sensation in attentive isolation with all of its attributes intact. The new logic asserts that sensations exist if the conception of their reality proves a fruitful hypothesis for a scientific psychology. The test of the reality of a psychological entity can no longer be an appeal to 'immediate introspection,' but is the systematic subsumptive power of the concept.

That the terms of introspectional psychology are not actual in experience but are conceptual reals is attested by the entire trend of systematic psychology. A sensation, as we shall see in the next chapter, is no longer regarded as actual but as a systematic construct. The sensory attributes have nowadays given way to abstract dimensions of consciousness. Perception is seen now to be a classificatory term, and there is no introspective difference between sensation and perception. In like manner all the other entities of conventional psychology—feeling, attention, idea, memory, imagination, action, emotion, thought—turn into conceptual reals that are not to be found in experience, but are inferred from it. Gestalt psychology gets along without these terms, but, as it develops, it has to create new ones, of which *organization* is thus far the most important. Organization is inferential. It is in this way that the paradoxical concept of the conscious mind gains validity. Both consciousness and unconsciousness are inferred, and the 'unconscious mind' is a reality that partakes of some of the characteristics of the other.

One serious difficulty that enters into all discussion of this kind is the two-faced meaning of the term *experience*. Experience is the ground of all scientific induction. *This* experience is prior to reality. It underlies physics and psychology, and enters into neither as a reality. Nevertheless, because psychologists have thought that experience enters immediately into psychology, they have spoken of their psychic reals as if they were experience. *That* experience is something different, a product of induction. *Real* experience is derived from *actual* experience. Real experience is what the psychologist knows about, but it is mediate and not direct.

We thus arrive at the first premise which underlies the discussion of this book. *Whatever exists as reality for psychology is a product of inductive inference*—usually from experimental data. To say that these realities are hypothetical constructs is not to alter the truth. The atom is a construct and a reality. Its validity is attested by its power of physical subsumption. The realities are always tentative and have to make their way and prove their worth. They are as temporary as all truth. There is no other scientific meaning for reality. If the psychologist will accept this premise, he will at last be ready to start his quest on a par with the physicist. If he will not accept it, he is landed in the esoterics of direct experience, and, if he then cannot realize his desire to make psychology scientific, he has no one but himself to blame.

If it be objected that this premise gives license to speculation, the reply is that speculation has always been free in science. The sanction for speculation is its fruitfulness, and the great scientists are those who have speculated wisely and successfully. The ultimate abandonment of dualism leaves us the physical world as the only reality. Consciousness will ultimately be measured in physical dimensions, and it is the purpose of this book to enquire how nearly we may approximate to this goal at the present time. We shall not always avoid the implications of dualism, and in fact we shall often have to begin with a dualism in order to annihilate it subsequently by the establishment of some identifying relationship between its terms. However, the goal is always the physical reality, the conceptual system that yields the most orderly view of nature. For such an aspiration no apology is required.

Psychophysical Correlation

We now come to the second matter of importance in this chapter—the nature of *psychophysical correlation*—and we must first examine the scientific fact regarded as an observed correlation.

The experimental method, upon which all science rests, is, logically considered, a method of the induction of a generalized correlation by means of controlled concomitant variations. In the simplest experiment there are always at least two terms, an independent variable and a dependent variable. The experimenter varies *a* and notes how *b* changes, or he removes *a* and sees if *b* disappears. He repeats until he is satisfied that he has the generalization that *b* depends upon *a*. The independent variable, *a,* can now properly be spoken of as a *cause* of the dependent variable, *b*. An observed correlation of this sort is causal in Hume's sense of *cause,* and the belief that cause and effect must be quantitatively equivalent in terms of energy is no longer rigidly held. The slight energy of a whispered insult may 'cause' a despot to move an army; the touch of a finger upon a stone may 'cause' an avalanche.

The total scientific process in which these correlations appear is both analytic and synthetic. It is analytic because inductive generalization requires analysis. We learn by experimental correlation that the cause of the quality green is the wave-length and not the energy of light, and that the cause of its brilliance is the energy and not the wave-length —approximately; and by the same procedure we learn to correct this gross analysis. Often when a correlation *a-b* seems to be established and then breaks down, we find that the difficulty lies in incomplete analysis; the correlation was really between *a* and *β*, which are sometimes but not always associated respectively with *a* and *b*. A great deal of scientific progress consists in analytical refinement of correlational terms.

However, the process is also synthetic. The simple correlation of *a* with *b* may be realized in the experimental moment, but a total experiment generally yields something more complex. Still at a very simple level we may establish by experiment functional dependencies of the form $y = f(x)$, which states the law whereby y changes when x is varied. In simple systems of fact, like the facts of the visual negative after-image, the correlations are more complex and involve several terms on each side, such as hue, brilliance, saturation, and duration. A scientific fact *is* a relationship, and the simplest fact is a correlation between two terms; but science is a tremendously complex correlational structure fabricated from these simple elements.

Let us now turn to the fundamental problem of psychophysics, which Fechner himself thought had raised and settled the question of the nature of the relation of mind to body. The Weber-Fechner function is $S = k \log R$, where S is the measured sensory intensity and where R is the measured magnitude (often energy) of the stimulus. We do not need to question the general validity of the law. We may suppose that the observer in an experiment is making intensive judgments of pairs of grays, which are controlled by black and white disks on a color-mixer. The law holds approximately for middle ranges of such a stimulus.

The first thing to note is that R and S are conceptual realities, that they are not 'immediate data of observation.' In observing R the most immediate datum is a judgment of visual spatial relations as one reads a protractor placed against the disks. One assumes that all angles on the protractor are equal and that they remain equal with any spatial or temporal change of the protractor. One makes photometric determinations of the reflecting power of the black and the white papers and assumes constancy for these values. One makes other assumptions in determining the energy of light that any setting of the disks provides as a stimulus. The value of any particular R is thus the result of an elaborate inference. We cannot observe energy directly, but we can observe it indirectly when we are satisfied to let the reading of the scale of the protractor stand for the energy which it implies. No stimulus or response is ever directly observed. We accept a sign for the reality signified, and, the more precise the quantitative work becomes, the more inferentially remote are the symbols from their realities. In quantitative work nearly all observation reduces to the judgment of spatial identity or difference of marks on scales.

This point has always been freely admitted of R, for R is physical and is thus 'mediate experience.' However, psychologists have generally failed to see that the same situation exists with respect to S. We can do no more and no less with S than with R. We can make judgments of identity and of difference between two S's, or of distances between two S's, and then we infer to a real scale of sensory magnitudes. Psychologists have been peculiarly dull about this matter. They have sought to appeal to 'immediate experience' in the case of S and have said that any one can see that a scarlet is not so many pinks, as if a greater magnitude must appear more complex to direct observation. Of course, if a scarlet is really so many pinks, its real quantity is the result of inference. A weight of 100 grams does not seem in direct observation to be 100 times as complex as a weight of one gram,—but then nobody has doubted the validity of inferring to reality in the case of R.

A very great deal might be said on this point, did it not take us too far from our primary concern. It is enough to assert that the most immediate data of observation yield the realities of physics, psychology, and psychophysics only inferentially. Even in the simplest case, as when an observer notes the presence of a tone, he is not merely catching a fleeting phenomenon and fixing it in a report. He is making an interpretative judgment under the influence of a particular intent. Any careful introspection in the psychophysical experiment reveals this fact. In all experimental observation, physical or introspective, one is working with realities by way of their symbols. One never comes directly to grips with that in which one is primarily interested.

Obviously Fechner established in certain limited cases the relation, $S = k \log R$. The formula is a statement of correlation between R and S. R causes S, and the way in which the magnitude of R determines the magnitude of S is stated. If the formula were accurate and the inferences involved were unchallenged, ought not the psychologist to be satisfied? He has a fact.

However, he is not satisfied. He immediately wants to know what, in a causal series, goes on between R and S. Even Fechner raised the question of "inner psychophysics," the question as to whether the logarithmic relation does not really belong between the excitation of the nervous system and the sensation. Causality may be only correlation, as Hume said, but no one is satisfied with causal action at a distance. Always he wants to make the causal chain temporally and spatially continuous, to avoid, in ultimate knowledge, gaps in the series.

Nowadays the gaps are being filled. Let us take the case of visual sensation. If we start with the visual stimulus-object, we know from physical and physiological optics what the situation is when the light strikes the retina. We know just a little about the process in the receptors in the retina and much more about the nervous impulses that follow in the fibers of the optic nerve. For instance we are pretty sure that a bright light gives rise to a greater frequency of discharges in the nerve than is the case with a dimmer light. We can trace the connections from the optic fibers to the thalamus and in some cases to the occipital cortex of the cerebrum. Certainty gets less as we go inward, but it is conceivable that some day we might establish certain physiological events all the way from the retina to the voci-motor muscles that utter the sounds that describe the stimulus. Where does the sensation appear in such a causal series?

In terms of Cartesian dualism there is no satisfactory answer to this problem. One thinks naturally of the conscious realities as immediate experience, as the impalpable and imponderable stuff of thought contrasting with a hard objective matter. Interactionism asks the psychologist to give such flimsy mind-stuff a place in the rigid causal system of physical events. It may well have been the disbelief that two such different worlds can interact that led men to say that cause must mean transfer of energy. The alternative is psychophysical parallelism: there is a physical event in the causal series, and the conscious event is separate but parallels it. However, parallelism is unsatisfactory, because with it the system usually will not close. Ordinarily there is lacking knowledge of the neural term that the conscious event parallels.

We can see this popular difficulty in the interpretation of the Weber-Fechner function. If the law means that excitation is proportional to the logarithm of the stimulus, there is no mystery; we have only a physical relationship. But, if it means that sensation is proportional to the logarithm of excitation, then we have, it might seem, a mystery, for we seem in some unexpected manner to have bridged the chasm between the two worlds of mind and body. Fechner thought he had.

However, mystery remains only so long as we hold that consciousness is direct experience. It evaporates as soon as we accept the conception of the present chapter about psychological reality. The psychological entities are just as palpable as the physical, which is another way of saying that the physical terms are just as impalpable as the psychological. At any rate, the data of introspection and the data of physics are at last coördinate and on all fours. We may see what can be done toward putting them into a single closed system, and such is the purpose of the present book.

Thus, in this view, a sensation is a real *datum* or event to be fitted into a closed causal system by the method of experimental correlation. In the early stages of research this view looks like interactionism, because we find stimulation causing sensation or sensation causing movement. With an increase of our knowledge of psychophysiology the view would come to resemble psychophysical parallelism, because then we should know something about a continuous neural series of events from stimulation to motor response, and the sensation would seem to parallel some middle part of this series. At this stage of knowledge the parallelism is not precise, and the sensation and its process in the brain cannot be fully identified. We could still keep our prejudice in favor of dualism if we wished. Ultimately, however, the ideal of parallelism must defeat itself. If we were to find a perfect correlation between sensation A and neural process a, a precise correlation which we had reason to believe never failed, we should then identify A and a. If introspection yielded A, it would yield knowledge of the nervous system; and, conversely, the physiologist would, in knowing about a, know about sensation. We must remember that A and a are both inferred entities or events; that they are real, but not in experience nor in a world that exists independently of its being known; and that, if A always means a, and conversely, there is no choice but to identify the two.

If this chapter presents an abstract and difficult beginning to the undertaking in hand, the author can offer no better excuse than that it has seemed to him necessary to clear out of the way some of the limitations that naïve dualism habitually imposes upon the thought of psychologists. While there is no possibility of disproving or proving dualism, the exposition of the present book is based on the assumption that it is scientifically more useful to consider that all psychological data are of the same kind and that consciousness is a physiological event.

Notes

On the psychologist's circle and the way out, see the author's discussion of this matter in *Psychol. Rev.*, 38, 1931, 177-182. Cf. G. A. de Laguna, Dualism and Gestalt psychology, *ibid.*, 37, 1931, 187-213, which deals both with the dualism of actuality and reality, and with the dualism of phenomena and the brain.

For Wundt's view that psychology deals with immediate experience and physics with mediate experience, see W. Wundt, *Grundriss der Psychologie*, 1896, Eng. trans., 1897, sect. 1. Avenarius's discussion of 'independent' and 'dependent' experience is in R. Avenarius, *Kritik der reinen Erfahrung*, 1888-1890; cf. W. T. Bush, Avenarius and the standpoint of pure experience, *Columbia Univ. Contrib. to Philos., and Psychol.*, 10, 1905, no. 4 (also *Arch. Philos.*, no. 2). On Titchener, see E. B. Titchener, *Text-book of Psychology*, 1910, sect. 1, 2, 5, 6; *Systematic Psychology: Prolegomena*, 1929, esp. 259-266. In the latter work Titchener gives excellent summaries of the positions of Wundt (pp. 98-113) and Avenarius (pp. 113-119, 134-138).

The present author favors Külpe's solution to the problem of the priority and posteriority of experience. See O. Külpe, Versuche über Abstraktion, *Ber. ü. d. I Kongr. f. exper. Psychol.*, 1904, 56-68, esp. 66-68; *Die Realisierung*, 1912-1923.

The belief in the availability of 'direct experience' is so firmly established that its denial almost inevitably provokes dissent among psychologists. Ever since Descartes the dominant doctrine has been that to be conscious is to be aware of being conscious. To experience is to know what is experienced. Mach quoted Krause: "Problem: To carry out the self-inspection of the Ego. Solution: It is carried out immediately." (See E. Mach, *Analyse der Empfindungen*, 1886 *et seq.*, and various Eng. trans., chap. 1, sect. 11.) But this is to say that there is no problem in introspection. Divergent data and the need of introspective technique, taken together with the rôle of the *Aufgabe* in introspection, should dispel so simple a view. What the author regards as the more sophisticated view is not, however, novel. Philosophers and psychologists have urged it. From a limited acquaintance with the writings of philosophers, the author selects the recent book of C. I. Lewis, *Mind and the World-Order*, 1929, as putting the matter convincingly. However, his own convictions about the interpretative nature of introspection were formed when he was an observer in an experiment of M. Yokoyama's; see the present author's note on this experiment, *Amer. J. Psychol.*, 35, 1924, 301-304. The general discussion of this matter is continued in chap. 8, pp. 222-229, 237f.

The monistic doctrine of the present chapter may be difficult because it runs counter to dominant belief, but it also is not novel. Any view of conscious data as responses to stimuli or as stimuli to motor responses is bound to fit the intermediate genetic stage discussed in the next to the last paragraph of the chapter. See, for instance, the author's discussion in *Psychologies of 1930*, 1930, 119-123, with which cf. R. S. Woodworth on mental reaction, *Psychol. Rev.*, 22, 1915, 22-27, and Gestalt psychology and the concept of reaction stages, *Amer. J. Psychol.*, 39, 1927, 62-69. Thus the author reads with sympathy and approbation E. B. Holt's *Animal Drive and the Learning Process,* 1931. Holt goes more to physiology than to introspection for his terms, but, if there are not two distinct worlds from which to choose, why should the term matter? H. S. Langfeld's presidential address before the American Psychological Association, A response interpretation of consciousness, *Psychol. Rev.,* 38, 1931, 87-108, is another sophisticated rejection of Cartesian dualism.

The concern of the text in theories of mind and body is purely negative. Interactionism, psychophysical parallelism, the double-aspect theory, the identity theory— all these views recognize a fundamental duality, two classes of events that interact, or are parallel with each other, or are different aspects of the same underlying *Ding an sich,* or are really identical although they seem to be different. There is no way of judging amongst these four views. Interactionism implies a break in the physical causal system and thus is rejected in most scientific thought. The other three views involve respectively the correlation of events, the correlation of aspects, and the identification of aspects. To the author a perfect correlation is identity. Two events that always occur together at the same time in the same place, without any temporal or spatial differentiation at all, are not two events but the same event. The mind-body correlations, as formulated at present, do not admit of consideration as spatial correlation, so they reduce to matters of simple correlation in time. The need for identification is no less urgent in this case.

Of course, as the text observes, these dualistic theories cannot be absolutely disproved. The point of view of the preceding paragraph is that the burden of proof is upon dualism, not upon monism. In the face of perfect correlation we identify, simply because we cannot differentiate. Thus red, being always red, is identified with itself, and all the symptoms of it are perfect correlates. If some one wishes to insist that red is a pair of perfect covariants, we cannot confound him. He is entitled to his view. But why should we assume two, when one is enough? If ever William of Occam's principle of parsimony was justified, it must be in this context. *Entia non sunt multiplicanda, praeter necessitatem.*

On formal identity, cf. L. T. Troland, *Principles of Psychophysiology,* III, 1932, 10, and references there cited.

Chapter 2

THE DIMENSIONS OF CONSCIOUSNESS

FOR all our disparagement, in the last chapter, of the dualism of mind and body, we shall not need greatly to diverge from the conventional vocabulary of the psychophysical parallelist. We may hold to the faith that ultimately the conscious reality and the physiological reality should merge into a single identity, and yet speak persistently of *consciousness*. To say with reason that a conscious datum is a physiological event would not be to make it any less conscious. The thoroughgoing dualist is the naïve behaviorist who ignores consciousness, thus asserting that there is something to be ignored in a world so different from his own world that he can safely disregard it. However, consciousness, though it may be imperfectly ignored, cannot be denied, and the hard-headed monist is forced to include it in his system. For this reason the present chapter is about the fundamentals of consciousness, as they enter into scientific psychology.

Sensation and Attributes

Scientific psychology began as introspective psychology, a psychology that has to do with the world of consciousness as distinguished from the physical world. John Locke (1690) called the contents of consciousness *ideas*. Hume (1740) distinguished between *impressions* and *ideas*. By the time of James Mill (1829), when the physiology of sensation had advanced and Sir Charles Bell had added a sixth sense, the muscle sense, to Aristotle's five, the distinction between *sensations* and *ideas* had become clear. It was Wundt (1874), the 'founder' of experimental psychology, who impressed upon the science the doctrine of elements, and made of psychology a kind of 'mental chemistry.' Sensations for him were the representative mental elements, and much later (1896) the feelings became for him an equally important class of elements. Thus, in the present century, introspective psychology (*e.g.*, Titchener in 1910) was holding to three classes of elements: sensations, images, and feelings. Some psychologists, inspired perhaps by the chemists' successes in filling in Mendeléyev's table, were seeking new kinds of mental elements. The most noteworthy example of this search is the effort of Külpe's Würzburg school (1901-1909) to find a new element of thought.

In the last twenty years the pendulum has been swinging away from the multiplication of mental elements. Külpe's failure to establish a new thought element started it swinging backward, or at least prevented psychologists from seeking further for new kinds of conscious data. The images never quite gained an independent status. Hume had called them faint copies of impressions, and Külpe (1895) had argued that they are centrally excited sensations. In a psychology that attempts to limit itself to a description of consciousness, sensations are but sensations whether they be aroused by central processes or by the stimulation of sense-organs. The feelings, too, began to give way before the sensations. James (1884) had held that emotions are characterized by their sensory content. Other psychologists (*e.g.*, Stumpf in 1907) had argued that the simple feelings are sensations. Finally Nafe (1924), in Titchener's introspective laboratory at Cornell, came experimentally to the conclusion that the simple feelings, pleasantness and unpleasantness, are simply bright and dull qualities of sensory pressure. No wonder Titchener could conclude (posthumously, 1929) that introspective psychology deals solely with sensory materials. Sensation had won the day. Conscious content is *ipso facto* sensory.

With *sensation* equated to *consciousness* the concept of sensation lost much of its significance. For the differentiation of conscious terms it was natural for psychologists to look to the attributes of sensations, as the different sensory characteristics were called. Sensations have always been distinguished by their qualities. Every sensation can be said to have an attribute of *quality*, which designates it as red or yellow or bitter or cold or C♯. Fechner (1860) first accomplished the measurement of sensations by measuring their *intensity*. It was natural, therefore, for Wundt to assign the two attributes of quality and intensity to sensation. Wundt dealt with space and time in the mental world as providing forms of sensory organization, but Külpe (1893) saw that *extension* and *duration* must be added to the list of attributes if spatial and temporal forms are found in consciousness. One can observe a visual extent as readily as a visual quality. Titchener (1908), facing the problem of the description of attention, which thitherto had appeared in systematic psychology in sinister dynamic guise, now concluded that sensations have an attribute of *clearness*, that a sensation in passing from the margin to the focus of attention is really changing its degree of clearness. Every one admitted the first four attributes and Titchener held to five. Later (1924) he named them *quality, intensity, extensity, protensity*, and *attensity*. By these co-relative technical terms he gave the attributes professional status in psychology, except for the fact that they were, in his opinion, no longer attributes, as we shall see in a moment.

As long as sensation was supposed to have only two

attributes, quality and intensity, everything was plain sailing. Quality was the individualizing attribute. An intensity was always an intensity *of* a quality: a mild warmth, a loud noise. The relationship was never reversed in thought; one never had a red faintness or a bitter strength. However, when extensity and what we may now refer to as protensity (duration) were added to the list of attributes, trouble began. One thinks of a perceived dot on a piece of paper as approximating a sensation, a number of dots as a number of sensations. On this view a row of dots would yield a row of sensations, and, since a row of dots very close together is a line, a line would also be a row of sensations. Yet to introspection a line is a sensation like a single dot in all attributes except extensity. It was essentially this logical difficulty that the school of form-quality (1890-1899) sought unsuccessfully to solve—unsuccessfully, because it supposed the form to be a new element, whereas the solution required an abandonment of elementarism.

In the first decade of the present century the sensation was regarded as an element because it was supposedly the simplest bit of conscious content ideally isolable in experience. The attributes are not really isolable, because, if you take away all quality or all extension or all duration from, let us say, a visual sensation, you have no sensation left at all. Nevertheless the attributes must be independently variable or they cannot be regarded as separate attributes. That which is essential to the existence of a sensation, but which can be changed without change of other characteristics, is an independent attribute of that sensation. In *logical* analysis the attribute and not the sensation is the mental element, as Calkins argued.

This preoccupation with sensation as the mental element caused psychologists for nearly half a century to overlook the fact that it is the attribute, and not the sensation, which

becomes the object of observational attention. In all introspective experimental work, where the degree of precision
is that of the psychophysical methods, the observer makes
his judgments of quality or of extent or of some other attribute, but not of the sensation as a whole. Külpe (1904)
realized this fact and raised the question as to whether the
entire sensation ever actually exists as such in consciousness
or whether it is not merely an inferred reality built up
out of attributive fragments which are realized at different
times. Rahn (1913) subsequently pressed this argument
home, so that even Titchener (1915) was brought to explain
that sensation is a logical systematic construct, while the
attribute is the immediate introspective datum. Thus it came
about that, just when the concept of sensation was losing its
significance because it no longer served to classify a part
of consciousness, the concept of the attribute provided
differentiae to consciousness. The attributes gained systematic importance because they were—belatedly—discovered to be the actual observational data of the quantitative
introspective experiment.

The reign of the attribute was, however, short-lived. The
phenomenology of Gestalt psychology has in the last decade
been making great headway. It doomed elementarism and
with it the sensations. With the sensation completely gone as
a useful concept, the attributes were left suspended in mid-
air, with no sensations for them to be attributes of. The
result was that the attributes also disappeared as concepts,
and description tended to become phenomenological after the
manner of the Gestalt school.

The author has no quarrel with experimental phenomenology as a temporary procedure in a young science. It may
afford a necessary freedom after a period of slavery to the
sensation and its attributes. However, freedom is dangerous
and readily runs to license. Phenomenology provides no rigid

rubrics for analysis and there lies in it the danger of a chaotic multiplication of descriptive terms and a consequent loss of the systematic integration that is necessary in a satisfactory science.

It appears that Titchener (*ca.* 1920) saw the way of adapting the newest view of the attribute to the new phenomenology by the doctrine of conscious dimensions, and it is the concept of conscious dimensions that the author sets forth in the following paragraphs. Unfortunately there is no way of telling how nearly the author's views represent Titchener's, for Titchener never published on this topic and the present writer knows what he was thinking only from casual conversation and hearsay.

The Dimensions of Consciousness

In order to understand the systematic rôle of the *dimensions of consciousness* we must turn to physical science, always the model for psychology.

As far as possible the realities of physical science are described by reference to the *c-g-s* system. Ideally the centimeter, the second, and the gram provide sufficient terms for the description of any physical event. Space, time, and mass are the ultimates. This ideal is not always realized. 'Qualitative' distinctions have often to be used, and, until very recently, the differentiation of the chemical elements was 'qualitative.' Moreover, any system is subject to change. Space and time are now in theoretical physics being thought of as constituting a single dimension. These exceptions and refinements need not bother us. Physics went far throughout a long period with its three dimensions, and a young science like psychology may do well to emulate it.

We must not let ourselves be confused by this use of the word *dimension*. It is plain that each of these fundamental dimensions of physics may contain dimensions within itself.

Euclidean space, which physics has used so successfully, is tridimensional. Time seems to be unidimensional, but, when we come to describe an acceleration in c-g-s terms, we find that it must be expressed in terms of centimeters per second per second or cm./sec.^{2}, so that conceptually we have a squared or bidimensional time. We shall need the same degree of freedom in establishing a set of conscious dimensions.

The dimensions of consciousness are the immediate successors to the old attributes of sensation. Modern psychology certainly needs four dimensions: *quality, intensity, extensity,* and *protensity.* Titchener's fifth dimension, *attensity,* has, in the view of the present author, become unnecessary. At any rate we can ignore it for the time being.

Sensation varies in *quality* when the change is one of color, or of the pitch of tones, or from warmth to cold, or from bitter to sweet, or from one odor to another. The exact nature of the qualitative continuum in each department of sense is disputed, but we shall do well to summarize the present status of the problem for each of the five senses without entering into the controversial details.

For *vision* the color pyramid (Fig. 1) has been supposed to represent a solid qualitative continuum. The hues are measured circumferentially about the center, and the red-orange-yellow-green-blue-purple-red series is the type of what is meant by a qualitative continuum. However, white, gray, and black are also sensory qualities. It is conventional to consider brilliance as varying vertically in the pyramid and to think of the white-gray-black series as qualitative. Thus saturation is left as the radial variable of the pyramid, and the line from gray to red has also been supposed to be qualitative. Hence it comes about that the conventional view posits three qualitative attributes: hue, brilliance, and saturation.

However, this view leaves intensity out of account, whereas

intensive changes, if they occur at all in vision, are obviously to be included in the pyramid. A recent conception supposes that the pyramid is a hollow shell and that radial lines in all directions from the central point are really intensive

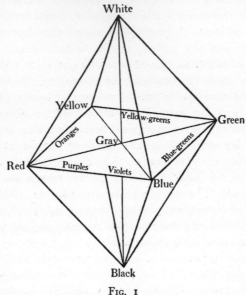

FIG. 1

THE COLOR PYRAMID

The color pyramid illustrates the qualitative dimension in the field of vision. In the conventional view the pyramid is solid. Hue varies circumferentially around the figure; saturation varies radially from the central axis out to the periphery; brilliance varies vertically. See the text for ways of regarding the pyramid as showing a combination of the qualitative and intensive dimensions.

continua. Such a view adopts G. E. Müller's notion of a constant gray (arising perhaps in the brain independently of stimulation of the retina) added to every other quality. Without the gray the central point would be simply a visual 'silence,' and from it would run intensive series of more-

and-more red or orange or pink or white or black, according to the direction of the line.

Many color theories imply a still simpler relationship, a system of seven qualities—a constant gray, and red, yellow, green, blue, white and black of variable intensity. Thus a poorly saturated red is a low intensity of red combined with the constant gray. A particular orange may have equal intensities of red and yellow, and a reddish orange a greater intensity of red than of yellow. This last view seems to the author the most obvious and the most probable solution of the relation of visual quality to visual intensity, but no decision is necessary here. We have merely to recognize that quality pertains to visual sensation, even though we may dispute some of the alleged instances of its variation.

In *hearing* the qualitative dimension is probably just the linear series of tonal pitches from the lowest audible tone to the highest. The noises can be regarded as complex combinations of incompletely established tones. The problem as to what makes the tonal series repeat itself in successive octaves, in spite of changed pitch, is far from being solved. Perhaps the continuum is a spiral and thus bidimensional. Because particular pitches characterize the different vowels, tones have been said to have a qualitative attribute of 'vocality'; but there is no evidence that 'vocality' is a new qualitative dimension. If tones have volume, volume must be an extensive dimension. Some psychologists think that tones vary in brightness and dullness independently of their changes in pitch and other qualitative aspects, but it is much more probable that 'brightness' is simply a better descriptive term for the high pitches, and 'dullness' for the low pitches.

In the *somesthetic* sense, orthodox opinion supports the existence of four qualities: pressure, pain, warmth, and cold. Such perceptions as roughness or wetness are 'touch blends' of these principal qualities—qualitative-intensive-extensive-protensive patterns. The internal organs and the mechanisms of articulation and equilibration furnish nothing new. Hunger, thirst, dizziness, and the perception of the movement of a member are all patterns of the fundamental qualities. Appetite does not even have a fixed sensory basis, but is consciously nothing but the knowing by a person of his own behavioral tendencies. Heat might be a fifth principal quality because it is aroused by simultaneous excitation of cold and warmth and is yet introspectively different from either; but the point is in dispute and need not be stressed here. Nafe has recently argued on experimental grounds that the only qualitative differences in somesthesia are brightness and dullness, and that the differences between pressure, pain, warmth, and cold are intensive-extensive-protensive patterns of brightness. This is a radical theory and still needs confirmation.

For taste and smell the qualitative continua are also uncertain. In *taste* there is no doubt about the existence of four principal qualities: sweet, sour, salt, and bitter. However, Henning has suggested that the taste continuum is areal, the surface of a tetrahedron with these four qualities each at one of the four corners (Fig. 2). In *smell* Henning has contributed the most modern and generally accepted theory. He has named six principal classes of odors: fragrant, ethereal, spicy, resinous, putrid, and burned. He has also presented a great deal of evidence to show that all odors can be thought of as located in the surface of a triangular prism, of which these six principal classes represent the corners (Figs. 3, 4). This prismatic system has been verified as an inexact approximation by several investigators.

In general, then, we see that the gross facts of the *qualitative dimension* are known for each of the five senses and that the details are disputed. The conventional view assigns four discrete principal qualities to somesthesia, and a plausible unconventional view assigns seven discrete qualities to vision. Taste and smell are thought of as involving areal continua, with four principal points of reference for taste and six for smell. There is no reason to suppose that these systems might not later dissolve into discrete qualities if

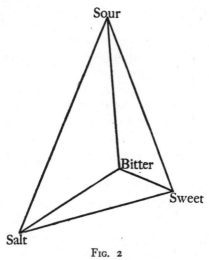

FIG. 2

HENNING'S TASTE TETRAHEDRON

The tetrahedron illustrates the qualitative dimension in taste. The figure is supposed to be hollow. After H. Henning, Der Geruch, 1916.

such a view prevails for somesthesia and vision. Hearing, however, seems to require a linear qualitative continuum, and there is at present no theory as to how a few principal tones could mix to give all the others.

It should be said that the differences between the senses are also supposed to be qualitative. The difference between a sight and a sound is like the difference between a red and a yellow in that it is a difference in the qualitative dimension.

For purposes of immediate description this view may stand, although we shall need to examine it carefully in chapter 6.

The *intensitive dimension* applies to every sense. Tones and noises may be loud or faint; tastes and smells may be strong or weak; pressures, pains, warmths, and colds may be great or mild. In vision intensive variation is obscured by the

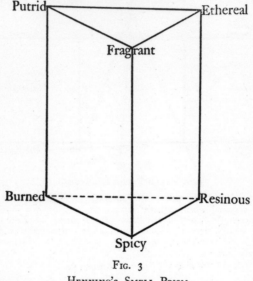

FIG. 3

HENNING'S SMELL PRISM

The prism illustrates the qualitative dimension in smell. This figure is also supposed to be hollow. After H. Henning, Der Geruch, 1916.

existence of the constant gray, which makes every sensory datum into an intensive-qualitative pattern. However, both common-sense experience and analogy with the other senses demand the validation of intensity for vision, and we have seen above how it probably enters in.

Extensity is most obvious as a dimension of vision and touch. The retina and the skin are areal organs, capable of differential stimulation by spatial patterns. The perception of spatial form is habitual in both senses. Presumably extensity is similarly applicable to taste, although spatial gustatory patterns are usually obscured because they are combined with tactual patterns in the mouth. Physiological considerations indicate that extensity, if it exists for three senses, should also exist for hearing, but the case is peculiarly

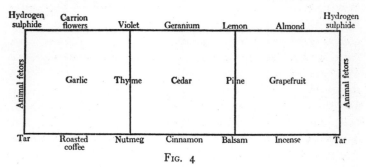

FIG. 4

THE SMELL PRISM DEVELOPED

The three sides of the prism of Fig. 3 are opened out, and examples of odorous objects whose smells belong in the various continua are given. The examples are selected from almost three hundred substances and objects which Henning places more or less definitely in the prism. The figure substitutes the more familiar grapefruit for Henning's shaddock, and almond for durian fruit, as well as giving specific examples for some of his general groups.

difficult. Tones have been shown to vary in volume or size, although some recent research fails to confirm earlier quantitative findings as to tonal volume. Of course sounds are localized, and the primary localization seems to be unidimensional in the right-left direction, the direction determined by the relative position of the two ears. In vision spatial patterns are projected upon an areal retina, and the visual perception of bidimensional form is relatively simple and accurate. In hearing the external auditory situation is effective only at two points, the two ears, and the simplest 'patterns' are linear. Presumably sounds have extensity, but since their extension is not representative of any external reality, it is relatively meaningless and thus does not come readily into observation. For similar reasons we are not likely to become aware of the extension of smells. We do not with smells have a purely olfactory localization because the two nostrils are located practically at the same point. With more noses we might do better, especially if they were widely separated upon the face.

Protensity offers few difficulties. Any sensory datum can vary in duration or can contribute to temporal patterns. The only difficulty that arises in respect of protensity is the question as to whether it can be 'directly observed.' The thesis of this book is that nothing is 'directly observed,' that every fact is an implication. One knows about protensity, in a particular instance, because one knows about it. The question as to *when* one observes a duration is to be answered by saying that one cannot accomplish the observation until the duration is completed. It is only the dualistic believer in 'direct experience,' who could argue that observation is instantaneous and that duration cannot be observed because it does not exist at any one moment for observation.

The transition from the doctrine of attributes to the doctrine of dimensions is so easy that one is apt to lose sight of the fact that the latter combines the freedom of phenomenology with the systematic organization of abandoned elementarism. The description of consciousness now resembles the description of a picture. With a picture one simply describes the qualitative-intensive-extensive pattern. For consciousness one adds the protensitive dimension and extends the qualitative account over the various sense-departments. The psychologist is not forced to make an artificial analysis into elements; nevertheless he assumes a responsibility to relate his account to the known dimensions of consciousness or to show cause as to why he departs from them in cases of necessity.

We are now in a position, not only to summarize the present discussion, but also to lay down the program for succeeding chapters. For all the objectivists and behaviorists have said, there would never have been a psychology if there had not been a problem of consciousness, and the way to make psychology 'objective' or monistic is not to ignore consciousness but to bring it into a monistic scientific system. Consciousness turns out to be, if one speaks accurately and carefully about it, sensory. A complete knowledge of the psychology of sensory data would be an approximately complete knowledge of consciousness. The sensory data are organized in respect of at least four conscious dimensions: quality, intensity, extensity, and protensity. We have nothing to seek further than the full account of mental organization in respect of these dimensions. At present the appeal must be in part to introspection, but we shall not be satisfied until introspective and physiological data have become so closely related that we cannot distinguish the one from the other. The immediate task before us is, therefore, the understanding of the physiology of the dimensions of consciousness. There is no prospect that psychology will shortly complete that task, but it must undertake it. In so doing much speculation must be risked, and many, perhaps most, of the hypotheses of to-day may eventually have to be abandoned. There is no reason to be fearful of speculation. A speculation is an interpretation, and in this sense even the introspective statement, "I see a green," is a little speculation. All observation is subject to the errors of inference. With such a defiant apology we may address ourselves to the task of formulating a physiological psychology of the dimensions of consciousness in the light of the scientific evidence available to-day.

Notes

Details of the historical development outlined in the beginning of this chapter can be found in the author's *A History of Experimental Psychology*, 1929.

Sensation and Attributes

The convincing identification of feeling with sensation came about, not from the arguments of Bourdon, von Frey and Stumpf (cf. E. B. Titchener, *Elementary Psychology of Feeling and Attention*, 1908, 81-121), but from the introspective experiments of J. P. Nafe, An experimental study of the affective qualities, *Amer. J. Psychol.*, 35, 1924, 507-544. These results, regarded at first with some skepticism, have been confirmed in other researches; see W. A. Hunt, The relation of bright and dull pressure to affectivity, *Amer. J. Psychol.*, 43, 1931, 87-92; The pressure correlate of emotion, *ibid.*, 600-605; Localization of bright and dull pressure, *ibid.*, 44, 1932, 308-313.

On Titchener's ultimate conclusion that the material of psychology is best characterized by the word *sensory*, see E. B. Titchener, *Systematic Psychology: Prolegomena*, 1929, 265f.

On the general systematic problem of sensation and its attributes, see Titchener, *Feeling and Attention* (*op. cit.*), 3-30; and for Titchener's conclusion that there is a fifth attribute, clearness, see *ibid.*, 171-206. Thus his book exhibits the state of sophisticated introspective elementarism as of its date, 1908. A decade earlier the question had been raised as to whether the sensation or the attribute is the true mental element. E. B. Talbot, *Philos. Rev.*, 4, 1895, 154-166, had given the argument for sensation. M. W. Calkins, *Psychol. Rev.* 6, 1899, 506-514, had said that the attribute must be the element. M. F. Washburn, *Philos. Rev.*, 11, 1902, 445-462, had performed the Hegelian synthesis by showing that either Talbot or Calkins is right, depending upon the definition of *element*.

Külpe's experiment (with W. L. Bryan) on the separability of perceptual characteristics in observation and his remarks about the *conscious actual* and the *psychic real* are to be found in O. Külpe, Versuche über Abstraktion, *Ber. ü. d. I Kongr. f. exper. Psychol.*, 1904, 56-68: but for his epistemology see his *Die Realisierung*, 1912-1923. The person who becomes interested in this systematic issue should certainly read Rahn's excellent critique. Rahn, influenced by Külpe and Stumpf, exposed the logical difficulties of the elementaristic position as represented by Titchener: C. Rahn, The relation of sensation to other categories in contemporary psychology, *Psychol. Monog.*, 16, 1913, no. 67. Titchener's reply, Sensation and system, *Amer. J. Psychol.*, 26, 1915, 258-267, foreshadows his doctrine of the conscious dimensions by admitting, so it seems to the present author, the essential validity of Rahn's objections.

It is regrettable that Titchener never published on the *dimensions of consciousness*. He introduced the terms, *dimension, protensity,* and *attensity* in a twelve-line note, *Amer. J. Psychol.,* 35, 1924, 156, but there is no explication of the doctrine. His students and his colleagues, including the present author, knew that he felt that he was in possession of the right key to the introspective description of mind, and the author has presented in this chapter what he believes to have been approximately Titchener's view. However, Titchener alive did not always confirm the author's interpretations of his views.

Dimensions of Consciousness

Papers bearing on the relation of *quality* to *intensity* in the color pyramid are those of K. Stumpf, Die Attribute in Gesichtsempfindungen, *Abh. d. k. pr. Akad. d. Wiss., phil.-hist. Kl.,* 1917; Titchener, *Amer. J. Psychol.,* 34, 1923, 310f.; F. L. Dimmick, *ibid.,* 31, 1920, 301f.; *Psychol. Rev.,* 36, 1929, 83-90; G. J. Rich, *ibid.,* 35, 1928, 311-318. For all this nobody seems to have said right out that the color pyramid is a hollow surface; that the center can be regarded as the point of zero intensity; that radial lines from the center to all points on the surface are lines of increasing intensity; that both saturation and brilliance, as well as their combinations, are matters of intensity; that the approach to

black and dark is an increase of intensity and not a decrease; and that it is only the persistence of the constant gray that prevents these relationships from being obvious. Yet Titchener and the others had something of this sort in mind. The author's view, that there are six qualities besides constant gray and that they mix in varying degrees which are matters of relative intensities, is so obviously the immediate consequence of theories like Hering's or Ladd-Franklin's that it has no right to claim originality.

Twenty years ago the question of the number of *tonal attributes* was a live problem. W. Köhler and G. Révész investigated the matter at length. The status of the problem is shown in G. J. Rich's investigation of the number of attributes by the method of liminal differences, *Amer. J. Psychol.,* 30, 1919, 121-164. See also R. M. Ogden, *Hearing,* 1924, 48-75.

The tale of the *somesthetic qualities* seemed to be fixed for the skin when Blix in 1883 discovered the pressure, warmth, and cold spots, and Goldscheider added the pain spots in the following year. It was supposed then that there are four kinds of receptors in the skin and that each of these receptors mediates one of these principal qualities. This theory persisted in spite of the fact that separate nerve-endings could not be established and that regions of the skin between the spots sometimes responded to presumably inadequate stimuli.

In the somesthetic field at large, however, the tendency has been to multiply qualities. In the second decade of the present century there were about a score of supposed somesthetic qualities. Since a list has never been printed, it may be well to give it here, together with the name of the investigator who established its claim and the date of his publication. About 1915 a psychologist might have made a reasonable case for the following twenty-one somesthetic qualities: (1) pressure (Blix, 1883), (2) contact (Goldscheider, 1884), (3) deep pressure (Head, 1905), (4) prick pain (Goldscheider, 1884), (5) quick pain (Becher, 1915), (6) deep pain (Head, 1905), (7) warmth (Blix, 1883), (8) cold (Blix, 1883), (9) heat (Alrutz, 1897), (10) muscular pressure (Goldscheider, 1889), (11) articular pressure (Goldscheider, 1889), (12) tendinous strain (Goldscheider, 1889), (13) ampullar sensation or dizziness (Mach, 1875), (14) vestibular sensation or sense of translation (Mach, 1875), (15) appetite (Carlson, 1915), (16) hunger, (17) thirst, (18) nausea, (19) sex, (20) cardiac sensation, (21) pulmonary sensation. The last six organic qualities depend, not on research, but on common experience; E. Meumann, however, in 1907-1909 listed these six and also satiety, fullness (of the stomach), and repletion. Ever since E. H. Weber (1846), sensory data like itch, tickle, and shudder have been repeatedly mentioned in connection with the *Gemeingefühl* or 'common sensibility.'

In the preceding list (15)-(21) can be asserted to be either inten-sive-extensive-protensive patterns of (1)-(14)—see the author's analysis of thirst, hunger, and nausea, *Psychol. Rev.*, 22, 1915, 306-331—or, as in appetite and sometimes in thirst, a knowledge of behavioral patterns. Cf. on appetite, E. G. Boring and A. Luce, *Amer. J. Psychol.*, 28, 1917, 443-453. Mach's vestibular sensation disappeared for want of support, and C. R. Griffith disposed of dizziness as a special quality, *J. Exper. Psychol.*, 3, 1920, 95f. There was never any good ground for believing that the qualities from the muscles, joints, and tendons (10)-(12), were unique, so by 1920 the list might be said to have been reduced to the first nine items, with some doubt as to whether the distinctions between the different kinds of pressure and the different kinds of pain were valid. It is this view that the somesthetic qualities are merely pressure, pain, warmth, and cold (and perhaps heat) that seems safest at the present moment.

However, Titchener tried to combine all the qualities into a single areal figure, *Amer. J. Psychol.*, 31, 1920, 213f., and now Nafe has argued on the basis of introspective experiments that the somesthetic qualities are only brightness and dullness, put together in intensive-extensive-protensive patterns. Warmth, cold, heat, pressure, pain and the rest are all qualitatively similar, differing only in pattern. See J. P. Nafe, The psychology of felt experience, *Amer. J. Psychol.*, 39, 1927, 367-389. The pendulum is swinging far back from multiplicity to simplicity. Cf. the further discussion of this matter in chap. 6 (pp. 171-181, 184-186).

The qualitative continua for *taste* and *smell* are Henning's taste tetrahedron and smell prism. See H. Henning, *Der Geruch*, 1916, 497-513 for taste, and 80-98 for smell. Since there had never been any such figures before and since smell had always been a great problem, these figures have been accepted *faute de mieux*. There have been a number of studies confirming the smell prism in the gross and contradicting it in detail. See M. K. MacDonald, *Amer. J. Psychol.*, 33, 1922, 535-553; A. E. Findley, *ibid.*, 35, 1924, 436-445; F. L. Dimmick, *ibid.*, 33, 1922, 423-425; *Psychol. Rev.*, 34, 1927, 321-335.

Extensity in the realms of vision and somesthesia is the basis of most of the work on space perception. In these two fields different laws apply, since contours are easily developed in visual forms, whereas tactual forms are not sharply bounded. In hearing the facts are not quite clear. See the detailed discussion of the research on tonal volume in the text and notes of chap. 4 (pp. 80-85, 116f.).

That *protensity* can become as directly an object of observation as extensity was shown by J. N. Curtis, Duration and the temporal judgment, *Amer. J. Psychol.*, 27, 1916, 1-46. The present book takes the position that a protensive pattern is real, that it is thus an implication, and that it therefore does not have to be regarded as existing at some instant for 'direct observation.' However, in general on the protensitive dimension, see chap. 5, pp. 127-145.

Chapter 3

INTENSITY

IN the older physiological psychology a convenient ignorance allowed a simple solution of the problem of intensity. It was supposed that an increase in stimulation means an increase in the amount or the degree of the nerve-impulse in all the nerve-fibers affected, a corresponding increase in the degree of central excitation, and hence an increase in sensory intensity. However, this simple theory became untenable when physiologists discovered the all-or-none law of the nerve-impulse. A single nerve-fiber responds to excitation with only one intensity. The case is not like that of an electric wire that can conduct currents of various amounts; the excitable fiber is more like a train of gunpowder which has the energy of 'excitation' inherent in itself, and which, if set off at all, transmits the disturbance by consuming itself with a maximal expenditure of energy that depends only upon the amount of powder in the train. The applicability of this principle to all sensory and motor fibers is no longer doubted, and the presumption is that it must apply similarly to the neurons of the central nervous system. Obviously some new theory of intensity is required.

However, before we consider the possibilities of a theory of intensity, we must take time to understand the nature of nervous excitation. Research in the experimental physiology of nerve-conduction has considerably extended our knowledge within the last dozen years.

36

Nerve Excitation

The *nervous system* is the chief integrating system of the individual organism. It is, in a sense, the organ of mind, because an individual can be said to be conscious only with the achievement of certain functional relationships which the nervous system makes possible. The nervous system consists essentially of a complex system of interconnecting neurons. A *neuron* is a nerve-cell with conducting fibers. The fibers that conduct impulses inward are called *dendrites,* and the fibers that conduct them outward are called *axons.* Ordinarily the dendrites are short, numerous, and branched. The axon is usually a long single fiber. However, the long *afferent* fibers that lead from the sensory receptors to the central nervous system are dendrites, and many of the neurons of the brain have elaborately branched axons and dendrites, which form a complex network. The ends of an axon are in close conjunction with the ends of dendrites, and this juncture between two neurons is called a *synapse.* The synapse presumably has numerous special properties, but its most important function is that it acts like a valve, allowing the nerve-impulse to pass only from axon to dendrite and not in the opposite direction. It is because of the connection of neurons through synapses that the impulse, under normal conditions, always passes in only one direction through the neuron.

It is conventional to speak of the integrative units in the nervous system as reflex arcs. The *reflex arc* consists of a *receptor* (the sensitive cell in a sense-organ), the *afferent fiber* (dendrite) that runs from it to the central nervous system (spinal cord or brain), generally one or more neurons in the central nervous system, and the *efferent fiber* (axon) that passes outward to the *effector* (the ending in a muscle

fiber or gland). A true reflex is supposed to be fixed, automatic, and unconscious, involving few neurons. The reflex
knee-jerk is even thought to involve only two neurons, the
afferent and the efferent. However, the reflex arc may be
very long and complicated indeed, and now-a-days psychologists speak of variable, learned, conscious reflexes as
conditioned reflexes. As a matter of fact, the conception of
the arc is too simple. Reflexes, even those reflexes that are
confined to the spinal cord, are not so fixed and stable as
they were once supposed to be. Usually many neurons are
involved, and not all of them are connected in a simple
series. We can hardly guess intelligently at what happens
in the brain, but we can see that the elaborate network
there would allow the formation of patterns of excitation
which would form fairly freely even though the fibers themselves are insulated from one another and can, on account of
the synapses, conduct in only one direction.

In short, the psychologist who adopts a principle of
parsimony in thinking about nervous connections, is almost
sure to go wrong. One modern view is that, in the new
nervous system just forming in the embryo, any stimulation affects, at least potentially, every effector, and that
specific relationships are established only as the system
develops.

The nerve-impulse in a single fiber follows, as we have
said, the all-or-none law. After the fiber has been excited
once, it cannot be immediately excited again. This period
of inexcitability is called the *absolute refractory period*.
The period may in a cold-blooded animal be almost as long
as 0.01 sec., and it is improbable that it is ever less than
0.001 sec., even in warm-blooded animals. We must remember this latter figure, for it means that in man we should
probably never, not even with the strongest stimulus, get
impulses aroused in a single fiber at a rate greater than one

thousand per second. After the absolute refractory period there is a *relative refractory period*, during which excitability gradually returns to the fiber. At the beginning of this period the fiber can be excited only by a very strong stimulus, and during it the strength of stimulus necessary for excitation is continuously reduced until it reaches the

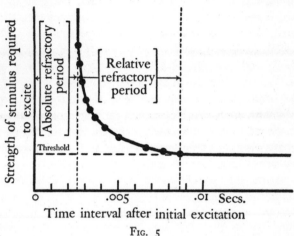

FIG. 5

EXCITATION CURVE FOR NERVE-FIBER

The curve shows the strength of stimulus necessary to excite a nerve-fiber at various intervals of time after an initial excitation. These values are for the frog. The times are shorter in warm-blooded animals. Adapted from E. D. Adrian.

normal threshold value. Fig. 5 shows how excitability returns after an initial stimulation. It is a consequence of this function that a continued strong stimulus can excite a fiber with rapid successive discharges, and that a continued weak stimulus gives rise to a slower rate of successive impulses. The possible rates of discharge of a fiber are, however, strictly limited by the length of the refractory period. No stimulus can be strong enough to arouse a series of impulses, separated by intervals shorter than the absolute refractory period. Unless there is summation, no stimulus is weak enough to set up a series of excitations, separated by intervals longer than the total (absolute + relative) refractory period.

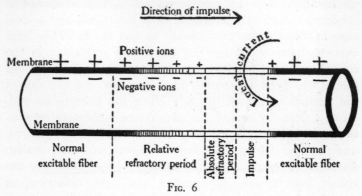

FIG. 6

MEMBRANE THEORY OF NERVE-CONDUCTION

Hypothetical and schematic. The semi-permeable membrane is shown in black with the positive ions on the outside and the negative ions on the inside. The impulse is traveling from left to right. It consists of a local current as the positive and negative ions unite when the membrane becomes permeable, and this current renders permeable the membrane ahead of it so that the impulse continues on. The permeable membrane is shown in white, and the membrane, which is being restored after the passage of the impulse, is shaded. Thus the diagram also shows the refractory periods. Adapted from A. Forbes, Foundations of Experimental Psychology (1929).

Physiologists have sought to account for these phenomena by constructing the membrane theory of nerve-conduction. The correctness of this theory need not concern us here. It is a useful picture for fixing the facts in mind. The membrane theory supposes that the nerve-fiber is surrounded by a very thin membrane that is permeable to small ions like the electrically positive hydrogen ions (Fig. 6). It assumes further that the nerve is polarized about the membrane, so that positive ions, passing through the membrane, are concentrated on the outside, leaving the larger negative ions on the inside. In the resting nerve the membrane maintains a difference of electrical potential between the outside and the inside. When the fiber is stimulated by an electric current or by mechanical action, the membrane is rendered completely permeable or is destroyed, and a local current flows from the outside to the inside. This local current, however, makes the membrane permeable in the next adjacent region and thus the site of the local current moves on. Such a situation is progressive and the site of the current moves all the way along the fiber to its end. At first, after the current has passed, the membrane remains ineffective, the difference of potential has been discharged, and the fiber is inexcitable in the absolute refractory period. Presently, however, it begins to recover, the membrane becomes impermeable to negative ions, the difference in potential is gradually reëstablished, and the fiber passes through the relative refractory period to the normal resting state again. The theory does not explain how this recovery takes place, but it is supposed to be a property of the neuron as a living cell. All these relations are shown in Fig. 6. Nowadays physiologists give a less thorough credence to the membrane theory than formerly; nevertheless this theory summarizes the accepted facts with sufficient accuracy for our purposes.

Now we know enough about the elementary physiology of the nervous system to come back to the problem of intensity, one of the four dimensions of consciousness. There are at present three important theories of intensity: (1) the multiple fiber theory, (2) the frequency theory, and (3) the volley theory, which is based on the first two. They all deal primarily with the peripheral nervous system, but they carry implications for consciousness.

The Multiple Fiber Theory

The multiple fiber theory supposes that intensity depends upon the number of fibers excited. The absolute threshold for intensity might be reached when only a single fiber is excited, and intensity would then increase by quanta as more-and-more fibers became excited by an increasingly energetic stimulus. The quanta would be too numerous and too small to be detected by psychophysical measurement, and intensity would thus appear, incorrectly, to be a continuous function of the stimulus with an infinite number of intensities available.

The theory demands that a strong stimulus should be capable of affecting a large number of receptors in the sense-organ, that there should be spread or irradiation at the periphery. In vision peripheral irradiation is suggested by the phenomenon of the 'magnitude' of the stars, where the perceived 'magnitude' is a function of the brilliance of the star and not of its actual diameter. For instance, the great star *Betelguese,* which is supposed to be about 240 million miles in diameter, subtends on the retina only an angle of about 0.047 sec. of arc, a distance less than one ten-thousandth of a millimeter and about one hundredth of the distance between two visual receptors (cones). It is plain that the first cause of dispersion lies in the defects of the eye as an optical instrument; these intense points of light upon the retina are blurred in being refracted, so that the bright stars are visible whether their images center upon cones or between them. However, there must also be irradiation in the retina; or else a stellar image, barely visible when centered upon a cone, would become invisible when centered between cones. Moreover, there is other evidence of retinal dispersion.

For instance, we find evidence in the experiment upon the least perceptible brightness. In this experiment the size and duration of the stimulus must be controlled. A large stimulus, to be visible, does not have to be so bright as a small one; nor does a stimulus of long duration have to be so bright as a brief stimulus in order to be seen. There is for intensity a summation within an area and throughout a duration. The same sort of phenomenon happens with colors. The retina is most sensitive to colors in a central zone. In passing from the center to the periphery of the retina we should ordinarily find certain colors diminishing first, and then others, so that in the outer zones there would be only the blacks, grays, and whites. A small purple disk, moved from the center to the periphery of the field of vision of a single eye, may turn dark blue and then black. However, the zones are hard to map, because the larger the stimuli the larger the zones. We cannot place a large sheet of purple paper before the eye and see three zones—purple, surrounded by blue, surrounded by black. The entire field is purple because the stimulus is now so large that the central zone of best color-vision extends to the limits of the field of vision.

Irradiation on the skin may be mechanical. The deformation of the skin increases with the pressure upon it, and the tensions within the skin must increase with the deformation. A very warm or a very cold stimulus would have a more widespread effect than a stimulus near the temperature of the skin. When the load is increased upon a needle as a stimulus to pain, it may penetrate deeper to additional nerve-terminations.

There is also evidence that the separate receptors in the skin do not act in isolation but are interrelated like the receptors in the retina. Two pressures at adjacent points, though each is too weak to be felt alone, may together give rise to a single sensation. Sometimes the relationship is reversed, and one fairly strong pressure inhibits the effect of another that occurs near it and at the same time. There are many nerve-terminations in the skin, and a great deal of the skin is supplied by fibers from more than one nerve-trunk. The terminations of the fibers are closely inter-penetrated. It is almost inevitable, therefore, that a more intense stimulus should affect a greater number of fibers.

In hearing, every stimulus inevitably comes into relation with a large number of receptors. The receptors are hair-cells in the organ of Corti in the inner ear. This organ lies on a membranous partition which separates an upper and a lower canal in a coiled tube, the cochlea. The tube is filled with a liquid lymph. The sound waves enter the upper canal through a membrane-covered window and escape from the lower canal through a similar window. When the upper window is pressed in, the partition-membrane is pressed down, and the lower window is pressed out; and conversely. The movement of the partition-membrane is such as to drag the hairs of the receptors across a fourth membrane that lies upon them, and thus to excite their nerve-fibers, just as touching a hair on the skin arouses excitation.

So much is positive anatomical fact. The exact action of a tonal stimulus within the inner ear is, however, disputed. One theory assumes that a weak tone extends only a little way into the cochlear tube, exciting a few receptors, whereas a strong tone extends far into the tube and excites many receptors. This theory accords well with the multiple fiber theory of intensity. The other theory of tone is the reso-nance theory. It assumes that different fibers in the mem-brane of the partition resonate to different frequencies of tone. Higher pitches are excited close to the entrance to the cochlea and low pitches at the other end. This theory lends itself best to the frequency theory of intensity, which we shall discuss presently, but it is not necessarily incompatible with the multiple fiber theory. It might be that an intense tone of 256 cycles would spread farther on either side of the fiber tuned to 256, and thus excite more receptors, than a weak tone of the same frequency. The only difficulty with this view is that an intense tone ought then to be a complex of pitches.

The multiple fiber theory has received support in the case of vision from a very interesting calculation by Hecht. Hecht observed in König's classical data on the discrimination of brightness, that there should be 572 discriminably different brightnesses from the least to the greatest. On certain other grounds he assumed that 30 of these brightnesses result from the functioning of the rods, the retinal receptors that mediate vision in very low illumination. That left 542 brightnesses for the cones, the organs of daylight vision. Hecht then noted the fact that visual acuity, the discrimination of spatial contours, increases with the illumination. In good illumination contours can be separately distinguished when separated on the retina by 1′20″ of arc, whereas in very poor illumination the separation between the contours may have to be as much as 33 times as great. 33 x 1′20″ = 40′, which represents about 0.2 mm. on the retina. An area on the retina, 0.2 mm. on the side, would be 0.04 sq. mm., and this area ought, from certain data of Helmholtz's, to contain about 540 cones. It is the approximation of this figure of 540 cones to the other figure of 542 brightnesses that seems to support the multiple fiber theory.

Hecht assumed that the cones are differently sensitive, and that a sample area of 0.04 sq. mm. would include cones of sensitivities extending over the entire range. In poor illumination only one cone in such an area might be excited, and, for spatial differentiation in the tests of acuity, the next excited cone would, on the average, have to be about 0.2 mm. away, *i.e.*, in the next adjacent area. As illumination increased, the thresholds of more and more cones would be reached, cones lying closer together would be excited, and acuity would become greater. Thus there might, in averaged results, be 540 quanta of acuity. There are, however, about the same number of quanta of brightnesses. Hence it is easy to suppose that increase in brightness comes about by the bringing into excitation of additional receptors, as increasing illumination continues to overtake their respective thresholds.

This theory requires further complication to explain how many cones in a single area can contribute collectively to a single intensity and at the same time act separately to give spatial differentiation in perception. Hecht assumes that the cones act collectively for intensity and differentially for acuity, because acuity is less when intensity is less. However, the facts upon which the frequency theory of intensity is founded, are just as inescapable as the facts of spatial summation and irradiation, and Hecht favors a combination of the two theories. Such a conclusion is wise, even though it must remain unsatisfactory until the way in which the two factors work together has been made out.

The Frequency Theory

The frequency theory attributes increase in intensity to an increase in the frequency of the impulses in each of the nerve-fibers involved. The researches of Adrian and his associates leave no doubt as to this fact in the peripheral nerves. They have recorded action currents in sensory nerves when a normally adequate stimulus is applied to the receptors, and they find that the action currents show a rapid succession of discharges which becomes more rapid when the stimulation is more vigorous. They have plotted the curves which show frequency as a function of stimulation. They have found this relationship for variation of tension upon a muscle, pressure against the toe-pad of a cat, light touch on the cat's toe-pad, pricking the skin, and moving the cat's hairs. They have also found it for variation of the energy of light in the eye of an eel. In one experiment this result has been obtained from a single muscle fiber, thus showing that it is not due to a 'volley' of discharges from a large number of receptors of different latent periods.

As a matter of fact, the result follows almost as a logical necessity from the nature of the excitation curve of the nerve-fiber. See Fig. 5 again. A strong continuing stimulus will excite a fiber early in the relative refractory period and give rise to a rapid succession of discharges. A weaker continuing stimulus will excite the fiber later in the relative refractory period and arouse a slower rate of discharges. The intervals between discharges will never be longer than the total refractory period; a weaker stimulus is below the threshold and does not excite at all. Conversely the intervals will never be shorter than the absolute refractory period, no matter how strong the stimulus is.

All this is true for a continuing stimulus. However, an abrupt stimulus of very short duration can also, as it is varied in degree, arouse different intensities in perception. This result comes about because the process in the receptor may persist longer than the stimulus. A quick thrust upon the toe-pad of the cat excites a process in the receptor that dies out relatively slowly. A stronger quick thrust excites a stronger process that fades away even less rapidly because there is more of it to fade away. Thus one always has enough continuation of the process in the receptor to give time for the arousal of at least a diminishing frequency of impulses in the nerve-fiber.

Fig. 7 is Adrian's summary of the facts. The stimulus is shown as continuous in amount. The excitatory process in the receptor is maximal at first but decreases continuously under adaptation. Hence the discharge of impulses in the nerve-fiber is rapid at first and slows down as adaptation reduces the excitation of the receptor. The 'sensation,'

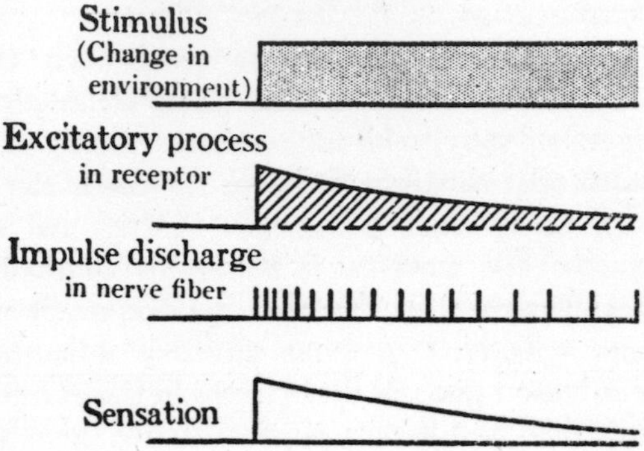

FIG. 7

FREQUENCY THEORY OF INTENSITY IN AFFERENT NERVE-FIBERS WITH A CONTINUOUS STIMULUS

The process in the receptor falls off under adaptation, the frequency of discharges in the nerve-fiber diminishes, and Adrian supposes that the 'sensation' diminishes continuously in intensity. After E. D. Adrian, Basis of Sensation (1928).

Adrian thinks, follows a smooth course like that of the excitation in the receptor. The sensation is caused by the frequency of discharge in the nerve-fibers, but since the perceptual process appears smooth to introspection Adrian draws the curve for sensation in this way. We shall do well to accept the facts indicated in the first three curves and to reserve judgment as to why the sensation itself seems smooth.

As we have said, there is no escaping these facts. On the other hand, the final theory of intensity would seem to have to be more complex. We have examined the evidence from summation and irradiation in the case of vision, and the need for a synthesis of the multiple fiber and the frequency theories. We know that there are similar phenomena in somesthesia, the sense which all but one of Adrian's experiments employed. The greatest difficulty, however, arises in the case of hearing.

For seventy years psychologists have been trying to achieve a satisfactory theory of tonal pitch. Helmholtz started the investigation (1863) with his resonance theory of hearing. He concluded that different fibers in the inner ear respond by resonance to different frequencies of the tonal stimulus. The structure of the inner ear is admirably adapted for this result, except that it is so tiny that the minute fibers might not resonate selectively without affecting adjacent fibers. There are at least 14,000 of these fibers in the ear and about 11,000 discriminably different pitches. Hence there are more than enough fibers to go around, and Helmholtz believed that there is a different resonating fiber, with a different receptor and a different nerve-fiber, for each of the pitches. Such a theory is consistent with the old, but now somewhat discredited, theory of 'the specific energies of nerves,' the theory that every quality has a place in the brain to which a fiber that functions for that quality leads. It was this notion of the physiology of quality that influenced Helmholtz. It will be seen that the resonance theory of hearing, in assigning different pitches to different fibers, can readily assimilate the frequency theory of intensity. A given pitch can be thought of as having its particular fiber, and, when this pitch is loud, the frequency of impulses in this fiber would be great.

However, the resonance theory of pitch has never been convincingly established. It explains the analytical nature of hearing, but a frequency theory of pitch has certain other advantages. The problem of the theorists has been to mate correctly conscious data with neural events. The conscious dimensions in question are quality and intensity. In the auditory nerve we have many fibers, every one capable of only one intensity of response but of various frequencies. Pitch may depend upon the particular fiber excited and intensity upon the frequency of impulses in it. This is the modernized resonance theory. Or intensity may depend upon the number of fibers excited and pitch upon the frequency of impulses in them. This is the frequency theory of pitch. The frequency theory of pitch seemed to require the multiple fiber theory of intensity. Conversely the frequency theory of intensity seemed to require the resonance theory of pitch. Neither view was completely satisfactory. Now, however, the volley theory has advanced the answer to this question, and we shall do well to turn to that theory instead of discussing further an old dilemma.

The Volley Theory

The volley theory is new and has been developed to account for certain new discoveries about the action of the auditory nerve. It is, for the sense of hearing, a combination of the other two theories, and we had better pass at once to the experiments that led to its formulation.

Wever and Bray, by an operative technique in the cat, contrived to hook a small electrode about the auditory nerve at the point where it enters the medulla. They placed another electrode somewhere else in the brain tissue; experiments showed that the location of the second electrode had no effect upon the results. Excitation of the auditory nerve creates a difference of electrical potential between these two electrodes, and, if the electrodes are connected by a wire, there flows in the wire a current of action corresponding to the excitation of the nerve. Wever and Bray amplified this current about 6,000 times and put it through a loud speaker in a remote room. They found that sounds reaching the cat's ear could be heard, without noticeable alteration, in the loud speaker. Speech was understood. Tones, clangs, beats between tones, and difference tones were transmitted with equal success. A variety of checks seemed to be conclusive that there was no simple artifact of electrical induction operating, and that the transmission of sounds depended upon the keeping intact and alive of the auditory mechanism in the cat's ear. The investigators obtained similar results for other mammals.

Wever and Bray were able in this fashion to transmit from the cat's ear to the loud speaker frequencies up to 4,000 cycles per second. When the tissues are made to 'die,' as from cutting off the blood supply, this effect ceases, and it may revive if blood is returned to the region soon enough. It is thus clear that the Wever-Bray effect is a biological phenomenon and not an artifact of electrical induction external to the organism. On the other hand, the electrical properties of dead and of living tissues differ greatly, and the critics of Wever and Bray have urged that the higher frequencies (above 800 cycles, say) are transmitted as a bio-microphonic effect of the stimulation of the inner ear and are not forwarded as action currents in the nerve-fibers. Be this as it may, the volley theory, invented originally by Wever and Bray to account for the transmission of high frequencies (and of speech) by the auditory nerve, remains very useful as a compromise between the two theories of sensory intensity, even though its original purpose may presently disappear.

The Wever-Bray effect seems to show a current of action at the central end of the auditory nerve corresponding to the stimulus-tone in the ear in both frequency and amplitude.

At first thought such a result appears to indicate that the stimulus is transmitted in kind by the nerve and that a frequency theory of pitch and a multiple fiber theory of intensity are to be preferred. However, Adrian's results for frequency as the correlate of intensity are not to be denied, and Wever and Bray proposed the volley theory to account for their findings.

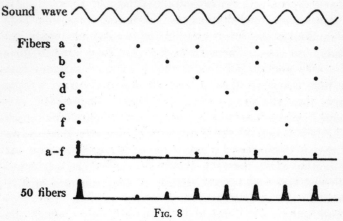

FIG. 8

VOLLEY THEORY OF PITCH IN AUDITORY NERVE WITH A CONTINUOUS
TONE AS STIMULUS

No one fiber responds with the frequency of the tone, but, except at the very start, the frequency is realized as the sum of the impulses in many fibers. After E. G. Wever and C. W. Bray, Psychol. Rev., 37, 1930.

The relationships that the volley theory assumes are shown in Fig. 8. At the top of the figure is shown a stimulus, the simple sine-wave of a tone. There is every reason to believe that this wave-motion is impressed, without great distortion, upon the hairs of the hair-cells, the receptors in the inner ear. However, the wave-form could go no further. A hair in bending would not excite its nerve-fiber until it had reached a certain critical point; then the fiber would be discharged in accordance with the all-or-none theory and would become immediately refractory. Thus every succeeding wave would discharge the fiber once, provided the period of the wave were not greater than the refractory period of the fiber. However, the human ear responds to frequencies up to 20,000 cycles per sec., and the refractory period of the auditory fibers cannot well be less than 0.001 sec. What happens with tones between 1,000 and 20,000 cycles?

Wever and Bray suppose, as Hecht did for vision, that the auditory receptors vary in sensitivity, and such an assumption is equivalent to saying that they vary in their refractory periods. (Consider Fig. 5.) Fig. 8 assumes that the most sensitive fiber, *a,* has a refractory period a little longer than the wave-period, and that it is therefore discharged by alternate waves. Fiber *b* in this figure is supposed to be less sensitive and is discharged by every third wave. Fiber *c* is discharged by every fourth wave, and so on. At the bottom of the figure is shown the sum of the discharges indicated above and also the sum of the discharges in fifty fibers of various excitabilities. It would be these sums that establish the total differences of potential upon which the current of action depends. We see at once that the staggering of discharges reconstitutes in the sums the original frequency, which no single fiber is capable of receiving. Only at the very start is there a lack of correspondence, and it is well known that it takes several waves of a tonal stimulus to establish its characteristic pitch.

Fig. 9 extends the argument to include differences of intensity. In the upper half of the figure the tone is weak and the discharges in every fiber are at a slow rate, in accordance with Adrian's theory. In the lower half the tone is loud, and the discharges in every fiber occur more rapidly, as Adrian's theory requires. The more frequent the discharges, the greater the number of coincidences and the larger the sums. Hence the amplitude of the current of action would vary with the amplitude of the stimulus, although every single fiber is nevertheless following the all-or-none law.

It is both a simple and a remarkable conclusion. Frequency and amplitude could be scrambled in the nerve, and yet an electrode merely hooked about the nerve could pick

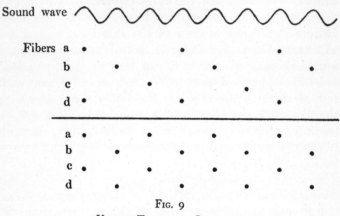

FIG. 9

VOLLEY THEORY OF INTENSITY

The figure repeats the schema of Fig. 8 for two intensities of stimulus. The stronger stimulus (cf. Fig. 5) gives a greater frequency of discharges so that the sums are greater. Thus the intensity of the stimulus is realized for the nerve as a whole although every fiber is responding under the all-or-none law. After Wever and Bray.

them out in their original form because the effect depends upon the sum of all the differences of electrical potential in all the fibers in the nerve. It is thus that the volley theory represents an intelligible combination of the multiple fiber and the frequency theories of intensity. The volley theory also restores plausibility to a frequency theory of pitch, in spite of the fact that frequency in the single fiber means intensity and that the single fiber cannot transmit frequencies as great as those of the higher pitches.

The bearing of the volley theory upon the problem of visual and tactual excitation is not yet clear. The volley theory has assumed that the process of excitation of the auditory receptors is purely mechanical. It is probable that the process in the visual and tactual receptors is chemical.

We can now summarize the present theory of afferent excitation. The frequency theory of intensity has been established, as far as research has gone, for the single fiber. Intense stimulation of the retina or skin leads to irradiation and more fibers are activated. Intense stimulation of the auditory organ may or may not lead to the activation of more fibers, but it does at least give a more frequent excitation of all the fibers affected. The volley theory shows that the frequency and amplitude of the stimulus may still exist by implication in the total auditory nerve, although neither is actually represented in any one fiber.

Sensory Intensity

But what about consciousness and the sensation? The older view of psychophysical parallelism sought in the brain for a physiological correlate of conscious intensity. The frequency theory would seem to call for frequency of central excitation as the correlate of intensity. The multiple fiber theory would probably require some conception of summation, so that equal impulses from many fibers could summate to give a great difference of potential in some part of the brain where the all-or-none law would not apply. Both theories seem to imply that a sensory intensity, existing at some moment, depends upon a physiological process localized at some spot in the brain. This atomistic view of consciousness does not agree with the dynamic nature of physiological processes, and, even when we assert the correlation, we are left with a vague sense of mystery as to how such a physiological event can imply such a totally different conscious event as lies on the other side of the gulf between mind and body.

The psychologist, who ceases to search in the brain for a replica of consciousness, will, however, see the significance of the volley theory for the solution of this problem. The simple electrode on the auditory nerve can pick out a frequency and a potential that exist only in the nerve regarded as a whole, and not in any of its separate fibers. Thus it would seem reasonable to suppose that intensity is some such totalized difference of potential in the brain. In this view, there does not have to be a single concentration of ions at some single spot. It is enough to suppose that the various increments of this difference of potential exist near enough together to have some collective effect. And the kind of effect is, of course, simply a response, interpretable in terms of movement and behavior, because our knowledge of the 'existence' of a particular intensity is little else than our capacity to respond discriminatively to it.

We are forced to the theory of intensity as a total potential because we cannot entirely get rid of the multiple fiber theory. We must assume that various adjacent fibers act together in producing a cognitive response. Such a view, however, forces us also to suppose that successive impulses, required by the frequency theory, can also act together. Summation of rapidly successive impulses at a synapse is known to occur, and it is probably in some such way that frequency becomes a difference in potential effective for cognition.

This view leaves us with a kind of gross localization of function in the brain. In the first place, it is plain that all the fibers or tracts involved in the process of being aware of an intensity (or of a difference between intensities) constitute throughout their course a locus of the mental function. The locus may change. For instance, Lashley has found that the discrimination of brightnesses by rats depends upon no single spot in the occipital cerebral cortex, but may be abolished by removing too much of the cortical tissue. When the function is lost by 'insult' to the cortex, it may be regained by reëducation, presumably by the establishment of a partly new locus.

In the second place, there is the problem of the location of the critical region where the differences of potential of many fibers act collectively to produce the discriminative effect. Lashley's experiments seem to imply that this region lies in the brain below the level of the cortex, since no one part of the cortex is a *sine qua non* of the discrimination of brightnesses. (Cf. pp. 104 f.)

Notes

The significance of the chapter will be more apparent to the reader who already knows the conventional elementary physiology of the nervous system. See almost any neurology or the chapters on the nervous system in any large physiology; *e.g.*, see C. J. Herrick, *Introduction to Neurology*, 1931.

On the all-or-none law and refractory period, see K. Lucas, *Conduction of the Nervous Impulse*, 1917, but remember that conduction with a decrement does not occur and was an artifact of earlier experimental methods. The research of G. Kato has revised Lucas's earlier conclusion. See also R. S. Lillie, *Protoplasmic Action and Nervous Action*, 1923.

The membrane theory derived support from the fact that an iron wire, immersed in acid, will con-

duct an impulse after the manner of a nerve-fiber. The acid oxidizes the iron forming an insulating film on the surface. The positive ions of the acid are on the outside, and mechanical or electrical penetration of the film starts a local current (see Fig. 6), which travels down the wire dissolving the film. The wire is then refractory until a new film has been formed on it. Cf. Lillie, *J. Gen. Physiol.*, 3, 1920, 128-143; 7, 1925, 473-507; and other references there cited.

Multiple Fiber Theory

The problem of the magnitude of the stars was discussed from the point of view of psychology in 1863: A. W. Volkmann, *Physiologische Untersuchungen im Gebiete der Optik*, I, 1863, 38f. A little later Bernstein developed the notion of central irradiation, in connection with the theory of the projection of peripheral space upon the brain and the theory of the threshold of consciousness: J. Bernstein, *Untersuchungen über den Erregungsvorgang im Nerven- und Muskelsystem*, 1871, 170-202. For more about Bernstein, see the text and notes of the next chapter, pp. 67-70, 115f.

For the effect of size of stimulus upon the absolute threshold of visual intensity, see P. Reeves, *Astrophys. J.*, 47, 1918, 141-145. On the variation of the zones of color vision with size of stimulus, see J. W. Baird, *Sensitivity of the Peripheral Retina*, 1905.

The clear-cut evidence for the summation of pressure stimuli still seems to be the rather scanty data of Brückner who was working in von Frey's laboratory: A Brückner, *Zsch. f. Psychol.*, 26, 1901, 38-47. There is a considerable literature on the summation of rapidly successive pressures to give pain, but it is only indirectly relevant here. Brückner thought that the simultaneity of two pressures might result in the inhibition of one, and that the reenforcement of attention would determine which one was felt and which inhibited.

The multiple fiber theory also finds support in Head's theory of cutaneous sensibility, in which the central point seems to be the separation of an *epicritic* sensibility from a *protopathic* sensibility. As sensibility returns after an injury to a nerve and with the regeneration of the nerve-fibers, 'protopathic' sensibility comes first and with it stimulation gives very intense sensations. With further regeneration the intensity of the sensations is diminished, and it is easy to suppose that other fibers with an inhibitory effect have grown back at this final stage. Even the present author, who does not agree with Head's dichotomy of 'epicritic' and 'protopathic,' has made the same assumption of an inhibitory relation between different fibers. See H. Head and W. H. R. Rivers, *Brain*, 31, 1908, 323-450, reprinted in Head, *Studies in Neurology*, 1920, I, 225-329; E. G. Boring, *Quart. J. Exper. Physiol.*, 10, 1916, 1-95, esp. 86-94.

For Hecht's discussion of the dependence of visual acuity on the variation in sensitivity of the visual receptors and its relation to the number of discriminably different brightnesses, see S. Hecht, *J. Gen. Physiol.*, 11, 1928, 255-281; or *The Retinal Processes Concerned with Visual Acuity and Color Vision* (Howe Lab. Ophthal., Harvard Med. Sch., Bulletin no. 4), 1931, 1-10, 25-29. Cf. H. Hoagland, *J. Gen. Psychol.*, 3, 1930, 354-359, and other references to Hecht there cited.

Frequency Theory

Priority for the frequency theory of intensity seems to belong to A. Forbes and A. Gregg, *Amer. J. Physiol.*, 39, 1915, 172-235, but E. D. Adrian and Y. Zotterman have done most to extend and establish it. See Adrian's excellent summary of the present situation, *The Basis* of Sensation, 1928. See also H. Hoagland, Specific afferent impulses and cutaneous sensibility, *J. Gen. Psychol.*, 6, 1932, 276-295; H. K. Hartline and C. H. Graham, Nerve impulses from single receptors in the eye, *J. Cell. and Comp. Physiol.*, 1, 1932, 277-295.

Arguments in favor of a frequency theory of pitch and a multiple fiber theory of auditory intensity were put forth by the present author prior to these researches of Adrian and of Wever and Bray: Boring, *Amer. J. Psychol.*, 37, 1926, 157-188. These views would need considerable revision at present, but the paper still shows the grounds for the multiple fiber theory of intensity and sets many problems that are ordinarily neglected in auditory theories. It was Max Meyer who first made the most plausible argument that the excitation of the inner ear would extend from the base of the cochlea an amount proportional to the amplitude of the disturbance: *Univ. Missouri Studies*, Sci. Ser., II, no. 1, 1907, 6-14. We cannot enter here into a bibliography of the theories of hearing. We must be content with saying that G. Wilkinson and A. A. Gray, *The Mechanism of the Cochlea*, 1924, have given support to the resonance theory of pitch by showing that the weighting and tension of the resonating fibers, as well as their length, must be taken into account. An excellent account of the mechanism of the inner ear is also given by A. Keith, in T. Wrightson's *Enquiry into the Analytical Mechanism of the Internal Ear*, 1918, 161-254. The reader should not expect to evaluate this controversy unless he understands the mechanism of the inner ear.

Volley Theory

For the experiments of Wever and Bray and their volley theory, see E. G. Wever, Action currents in the auditory nerve in response to acoustical stimulation, *Proc. Nat. Acad. Sci.*, 16, 1930, 344-350; Wever and C. W. Bray, Nature of acoustic response: the relation between sound frequency and the frequency of impulses in the auditory nerve, *J. Exper. Psychol.*, 13, 1930, 373-387; Wever and Bray, Present possibilities for auditory theory (includes formulation of the volley theory), *Psychol. Rev.*, 37, 1930, 365-380; Wever, Impulses from the acoustic nerve of the guinea pig, rabbit and rat, *Amer. J. Psychol.*, 43, 1931, 457-462; Wever and Bray, Auditory nerve responses in the reptile, *Acta Oto-Laryngol.*, 16, 1931, 154-159. The Wever-Bray effect has been verified by several investigators, and the suggestion that it may be bio-microphonic is only very recent. The references to the verifications, as well as the argument for the bio-microphonic action, are given by G. Kreezer, A critical examination of the investigations of auditory action currents, *Amer. J. Psychol.*, 44, 1932, 638-676. The matter is still highly controversial, and the author has taken advantage of his proof sheets to add this very recent reference to Kreezer and somewhat to amplify the text.

Sensory Intensity

There is nothing startling to modern physiology in the suggestion that the physiological account of the intensity of a sensation should be the description of events which, regarded in separation from one another, are differently localized in the brain, although their total effect may have a more specific locus. Cf. the way in which total dynamic organization is regarded in the theory of physiological gradients: C. M. Child, *Physiological Foundations of Behavior*, 1924. K. S. Lashley has cautiously faced and discussed this sort of problem in his *Brain Mechanisms and Intelligence*, 1929, 157-174, esp. 168-170.

Lashley suggests that the cerebral cortex functions as a whole in memory and learning, that loss of habits is roughly proportional to the amount of cortical tissue removed, and that speed of relearning varies inversely with the amount of tissue removed. The occipital cortex is best adapted for these functions in the case of the discrimination of brightnesses, but rats with the entire occipital cortex extirpated have nevertheless learned, slowly, to discriminate brightnesses as accurately as normal rats. Thus the 'sensation' itself would require a subcortical localization, even though the awareness of sensations would depend upon the cortex. See K. S. Lashley, *op. cit.;* Cerebral control versus reflexology, *J. Gen. Psychol.,* 5, 1931, 3-18; Mass action in cerebral function, *Science,* 73, 1931, 245-254, esp., 248f., and references

there cited. The last article is the most explicit on the matter in hand.

Weber-Fechner Law

There has been so much discussion of the Weber-Fechner law in psychology that some mention of it seems necessary here. The law is a statement of the dependence of sensory intensity upon the magnitude of the stimulus. The following positive and negative statements about it are true at the present time. (1) Sensory intensity practically always follows a law of diminishing returns when regarded in relation to the increase of the magnitude of the stimulus. (2) The formula *Intensity of sensation* = k log (*stimulus*), or S = k log R, habitually fails at the two extremes and probably is not exact even in the middle ranges. (3) In some cases data fit better a sigmoid or ogival function between S and log R (the relationship that would be a straight line for S = k log R). It is obvious that no general formula can be written so long as the units of the stimulus are not generally defined, and they never have been defined. R is not, as some suppose, always expressed in terms of energy; actually it is expressed in ergs or grams or often, as in testing the law for taste or smell, in arbitrary units of some instrument. The wonder is, not that a definite formula fails to be satisfied, but that the general condition of diminishing returns is usually found. See on points (1)-(3), H. Hoagland, The Weber-Fechner law and the all-or-none theory, *J. Gen.*

Psychol., 3, 1930, 351-373. Cf. also Hecht, visual discrimination of intensity and the Weber-Fechner law, *J. Gen. Physiol.*, 7, 1924, 235-267.

In this recent discussion of the Weber-Fechner law there is one suggestive point for our purposes. The physiologists are usually considering some form of nervous excitation as a function of the stimulus: $E = f(R)$, let us say. Suppose that this function were an ogive when plotted between E and log R and suppose R were so defined that the generalization was established for some class of phenomena. The psychologist might object and say, "But E is not the sensation. It is a neural process." However, Hecht has gone to König's data, has come away with genuine sensations, S, got by introspection, and has then shown them to fit an ogive. If both E and S give ogives, the implication would be that S is at least proportional to E, and it may be that S *is* E. Unfortunately we are not yet in a position to draw such an inference, but the method would become interesting if only R could be generalized for all departments of sense.

Chapter 4

EXTENSITY

THE perception of spatial extent as size, shape, and position is largely a matter of the organization of consciousness in the dimension of extensity. We shall understand the present status of this problem better, if we begin by sketching its history.

The Psychological Problem of Space

The old naïve view of these matters was that the nerves are conductors of the properties of objects to the brain, where the sensorium somehow apprehends what the nerves present to it. It was plain that touch and vision are spatial senses, because their organs are surfaces richly supplied with nerve-fibers. An object acting upon the skin or an illuminated object imaged upon the retina gives rise to a spatial pattern of excitation of the nerves, with the consequent implication that the sensorium might perceive the pattern as such. When it was realized from physiological optics that the image on the retina is inverted, the physiologists raised the question as to why we do not see everything upside down. The fact that the inversion of the retinal image still seems to so many persons to present something paradoxical shows how natural this old naïve view was, for there is nothing in modern psychological conceptions to lend a shred of significance or interest to the problem.

However, there was in this primitive view a hint of the

projection theory, which became explicit in the nineteenth century. We find that theory in an intermediate stage implied by Johannes Müller (*ca.* 1838). Müller's doctrine of the specific energies of nerves was a theory of the qualitative differences between the senses. It asserted that the mind is aware of the state of the nerves and not of the properties of external bodies. Pressure on the eyeball is sensed as light because it affects the optic nerve; light on the skin is sensed as warmth because it affects the tactual nerves. Müller was denying that the nerves transmit any properties other than their own energies, which are specific for each of the five senses. He thus implied that there is within the brain a perceiving mind that can become directly aware of the state of the nerves which end in the brain. This conception is not a projection theory of quality, but it defines, as it were, the 'envelope' which contains the mind and upon which characteristics of external objects must be 'projected' if they are to be accessible to the mind.

On the other hand, Müller's view of space perception was essentially the projection theory. The visual or tactual stimulus impresses its spatial pattern upon the retina or the skin, as the case may be, and the nerves conduct the pattern to the sensorium. It was Müller's study of binocular vision that pointed to this view. He knew about the horopter and about corresponding points on the two retinas. He knew that the optic nerves divide at the optic chiasma, that some fibers cross and some do not, and he concluded that fibers from one side of the field of vision go to the same side of the brain, and that fibers from corresponding points in the two eyes lead to the same point in the brain. A notion of this sort is almost equivalent to saying that the retinas are projected in their spatial relationships upon that field in the brain which is the 'envelope' of the mind.

The explicit form of the projection theory is to be found

in the ideas of Bernstein (1868), but we must reserve this discussion until the next section.

The new physiological psychology was ushered in at the middle of the nineteenth century with considerable interest in the problems of space perception, and considerable discussion of the theoretical problems of nativism and geneticism. It was Lotze in his *Medicinische Psychologie* (1852) who put forth his famous theory of local signs and laid the foundations of the genetic theory, which Wundt and many others held later. The genetic theory of space makes the projection theory unnecessary. It assumes that every point has a conscious local sign which identifies it qualitatively without in itself placing the point spatially. According to the genetic theory we have nothing to start with but an unorganized congeries of local signs. However, these signs can be supposed to get themselves ordered into a spatial continuum as the result of the experienced relationships that occur in the continuous movement of stimulation across the skin or the retina. We need go no further into the genetic theories nor need we undertake to understand how the kinesthesis of movement came to be essential to all of them; it is enough to see that a fundamental tradition of the psychology of the later nineteeth century—the tradition of Lotze, Helmholtz, and Wundt—got along without believing that the structure of space is given immediately to the mind in the native constitution of the psychophysical organism.

Nativism, on the other hand, fitted in much more satisfactorily with the projection theory. Nativists, like Hering (1864) and Stumpf (1873), held that the structure of space is inherent in the sensations themselves. Hering assumed that every retinal point has three conscious characteristics—height, breadth, and depth. The signs for height and breadth, he supposed, fixed a spot in the bidimensional field of vision, while the disparity between the signs for depth furnished the basis for localization in the third dimension when there is binocular parallax. Nowadays such a view seems absurdly naïve, but it was a great advance over Johannes Müller's. Müller thought of the mind as in the brain, perceiving what the nerves brought to it. Hering thought of the mind as being sensory experience, and thus he tried to fabricate the structure of space out of conscious sensory data. Paradoxical as it may seem, Hering, the physiologist, working in what was then called "physiological psychology," saw more importance in a thoroughgoing psychology of conscious phenomena than do the modern psychologists, who are not physiologists and who no longer speak habitually of "physiological psychology." Nineteenth century dualism in psychology told against physiological interpretation in many cases where twentieth century monism indicates the physiological approach. Except for this difference one might suppose that Hering would have couched his nativism in the simple physiological terms of the projection theory, for what nativism could be simpler than the actual projection of the spatial relations at the periphery upon the brain itself?

In the present century the most important development in the psychology of space has been the development and acceptance of the concept of extensity as an immediate phenomenal datum. We have already seen how this result came about (pp. 19f.). The doctrine of form-quality (1890 *et seq.*), while it was in error in supposing that form is a separate mental element based upon other more fundamental sensory elements, nevertheless correctly anticipated the future in asserting the phenomenal status of form as comparable with the phenomenal status of quality. It was a similar insight that influenced Külpe to assert that extensity is an attribute of sensation, an attribute coördinate with quality and intensity, and to characterize sensory spatial organization as spatial colligation. Titchener later followed Külpe in respect of extensity as a sensory attribute. He believed that bare extensity must be native to sensation, yet held to a genetic theory of the way in which the structure of space is worked up in experience. However, up to this time (*ca.* 1910) introspectional psychology never seemed able to free itself completely from Wundtian elementarism in which a form seemed to be the sum of its parts. While it is true that the proponents of form-qualities and Külpe and Titchener did not think of a line as a continuous row of sensations, still the significance of this fact seems not to have become apparent until it was exhibited by Gestalt psychology. Wertheimer and Koffka made it quite clear that extent is as primary as quality; that it can, like intensity, vary in degree; and that form is merely mental organization given in the dimension of extensity. It was Titchener who supplied the word *dimension,* but it was the Gestalt psychologists who forced the new conception upon psychology by reiteration.

Although Külpe and Titchener thought of extensity as immediate, primitive, and phenomenal, they realized that localization may often be mediate and secondary, for a tactual sensation is usually localized either by touching or visualizing the supposed point of stimulation. These motor and visual mechanisms are obviously touched off by association, and the associative context must be supposed to be specifically determined by particular fibers leading from particular points at the periphery. Külpe and Titchener are best summarized by saying that the points of stimulation have 'unconscious local signs,' and that they are independently capable of giving rise to specific localizing contexts, although the sensory core of the experience is not specific as to locus. Such a view just misses being a projection theory. It assumes that every peripheral point has the capacity for specific connections in the brain, but it does not assume that the terminations in the brain maintain the spatial relation of the fibers at the periphery. The Gestalt psychologists went further, as we shall see presently.

We may summarize this brief sketch of a confused and ponderous literature by saying that the attack upon the psychological problem of space has resulted, after four score years of discussion, in the acceptance of the notion that organized extensity is phenomenally given. Thus nativism seems to have triumphed as to the capacity to perceive spatial form in respect of its internal relations, although geneticism may still account for many phenomena of localization. This particular issue no longer interests psychologists, but it has been worth considering because the view of space that is consistent with the nativistic hypothesis tends also to link itself with a physiological hypothesis, where perceived space is correlated with spatial relations established in the nervous system without learning. Thus the modern view of phenomenal space tends to look for support to some sort of projection hypothesis.

The Projection Theory

To suppose that spatial patterns of excitation at the periphery—on the skin or the retina—are projected by the nerve-fibers upon some central field of excitation in the brain is to hold a theory that is both pretty and improbable in this simple, unmodified form. Nevertheless we shall come most readily to an understanding of the business in hand, if we consider first Bernstein's naïve projection theory, and then see how it has been qualified.

Bernstein's theory is illustrated in Fig. 10. The nerve-fibers at the periphery, P, pass to the central field of projection, C, in such a way that the spatial relations at the periphery are not altered at the brain. To this simple notion of projection, Bernstein added the conception of central dispersion: stimulation at *a*, projected upon *a'*, spreads as in *A*.

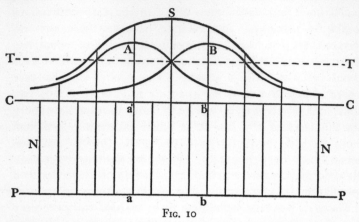

Fig. 10

BERNSTEIN'S THEORY OF CENTRAL PROJECTION AND IRRADIATION

P=periphery or sense-organ, like the retina or the skin. *C*=central nervous system associated with consciousness. The spatial relations of stimulation at *P* are supposed to be projected along the nerve-fibers, *N*, upon the center, *C*, so that similar relationships occur at *P* and *C*. However, there may be irradiation or dispersion at the center. Stimulation of a fiber at *a* gives rise to the dispersed excitation indicated by the curve *A*, which centers upon *a'*, the point of projection of *a*. Similarly stimulation of *b* gives the dispersion *B* about *b'*. Thus, if *a* and *b* were stimulated together, the result at the center would be *S*, the sum of *A* and *B*. *T* represents the threshold of consciousness and has been added to Bernstein's figure. If the stimulation of *a* and *b* were small, *A* and *B* might both lie entirely below *T*; stimulation would be said to be subliminal. Nevertheless subliminal *A* and *B* might summate to give a supraliminal *S* above *T*.

The theory has been used to explain the facts of the limen of dual impression upon the skin. It is well known that two stimulating points close together upon the skin give rise to the perception of a single point. Fig. 10 might illustrate just this case. Stimulations at *a* and at *b* set

up the central excitations, *A* and *B,* which, occurring simultaneously, summate as *S.* Perception corresponds to *S,* a
larger, blunter impression, but nevertheless a single point.
If *a* and *b* were far apart the central excitations, *A* and *B,*
would not affect each other, and two separate impressions
would be perceived. Intermediate between these two extremes there are, however, the equivocal cases of incomplete
separation, where the perceptual pattern is described as a
'dumb-bell' or 'double paddle.' This would be the case
where *A* and *B* are so far apart as to give (Fig. 10) two
'hills' connected by a 'saddle.' Thus Bernstein's theory
fits the facts of the two-point limen excellently, although
these facts do not, of course, prove the theory. The dispersion may be peripheral; it might be nothing other than
the deformation of the skin. The principle of projection is a
speculation.

There is, however, something to be learned from the very
fact that Bernstein's would be a satisfying theory if projection and dispersion were true. This theory asserts that
the pattern of the stimulus is maintained by projection and
altered by dispersion in the pattern of central excitation
which itself *is like* the perceptual pattern yielded by introspection. The theory seeks to explain the relationship of
the perceptual pattern to the stimulus by expounding the
nature of the dependence of the central excitation upon
the stimulus. Why should any one suppose that the establishment of the nature of the correlation between central excitation and stimulus would imply a theory of the correlation
between perceptual pattern and stimulus? Obviously such
a view becomes a satisfying theory only if there is an approximate identification of perceptual pattern with central
pattern of excitation or if the relationship between the two
data is known. One must identify conscious datum with
cerebral excitation or at least assume that the two closely

resemble each other, or one must abandon Bernstein's theory.

It is in this surreptitious way that the projection theory has come to imply the theory of psychophysiological correspondence. The parallelists among the psychologists have tended most naturally to think of the parallelism as applying in detail with a one-to-one correspondence between conscious and cerebral events and also with a similarity in the structural constitution of the two kinds of events. It is true that Fechner is a notable exception to this tendency; he argued that the logarithmic dependency which the Weber-Fechner law expresses truly describes the relation of sensation to the "inner" physiological event. G. E. Müller, however, tried to localize this logarithmic functional dependency in the nervous system, and Wundt tried to localize it in the conscious mind. Both Müller and Wundt, therefore, held to the belief in a direct correspondence between the sensation and its physiological basis. For such parallelists correspondence is not to be confused with identity; nevertheless the one view easily passes over into the other. Psychologists seem always to demand proof of any complex or involved relationship between mind and body but to accept a simple proportionality or correspondence as probable without proof. Why should they, unless they are influenced by the possibility of an ultimate demonstration of identity between the two?

The physiologists have also unintentionally tended to support this theory of correspondence. Since they are not ordinarily concerned with the use of the introspective method, they naturally regard the "mind" as cerebral. Thus they sometimes substitute neural excitatory terms for introspective terms, just as if they believed in the theory of direct correspondence. The latest example of this confusion has been the attempt of certain physiologists to reinterpret the

Weber-Fechner function, which formulates the relation between the intensity of sensation and the magnitude of
stimulus. These physiologists find that the relation between
excitation and stimulation sometimes follows a law that
resembles Fechner's law but differs significantly from it.
Then they argue that Fechner's law is incorrect. Now we
know from psychological experimentation that Fechner's law
is not correct, but this argument of the physiologists cannot
be, of course, an argument against Fechner's law unless
it accepts the principle of direct correspondence. (Cf. pp. 6of.)

We come in this fashion to a partial understanding of the
way in which the modern theory of extensity has come about.
The present-day attitude in this matter is the direct consequence of the theory of projection which has carried with
it the theory of correspondence. For the most part both
theories have remained implicit in psychological thought
even in the face of occasional explicit denial. The psychologists, as a matter of fact, were faced with a dilemma.
They wanted to deal physiologically with the problem of
the perception of space and they also wanted to avoid
vague physiological speculation. Perhaps one should not be
surprised that, in the face of such conflict, the physiological
theory more often remained implicit and escaped the ex-
posure of explication.

On the other hand, not all of this theorizing has been mere
guesswork. The validity of a theory is largely measured
by its capacity to subsume observed fact without contradicting other observed fact. Let us, therefore, examine these
physiological concepts.

Certainly in the field of vision the gross fact of projection has been accepted for more than a century. There
is nothing at all improbable about the contention that corresponding points of the two retinas are projected upon some
common point or, in more modern terminology, that the

paths from two corresponding points finally fuse in a common path. It is not merely that the anatomy of the optic chiasma and the pathology of hemianopia support this view. The inference is almost unavoidable when we remember that, although visual localization is otherwise very accurate indeed, stimulation of one retina cannot be distinguished by introspection from stimulation of the other and there is only one field of vision. There are two alternative formulas for this situation. We may say that the two retinas are projected upon a common central field and that therefore the field of vision is one; or we may say that, since the systems of paths from the two retinas join in a corresponding system of common paths, it is not possible to condition a response that discriminates one retina from the other.

In the field of touch it is plain that afferent paths do not fuse into common paths before they reach the point where the connections effecting localization can be made. Tactual localization is a context, usually a context of visual imagery added to the sensory core or a context of a localizing movement which indicates the point stimulated. Localization may be learned or 'conditioned'; perhaps it is always learned in the lifetime of the individual.

Localization requires that spatial differentiation of receptors at the periphery should be reflected in differentiation of paths at the center. That there is actually an approximate projection is indicated by the fact that large errors of localization are less common than small. If the paths maintained their independence but were all mixed up at the region of the localizing connections, then, if there were any errors in localization, they would be just as likely to be large as small. Two spots on the same forearm might be confused no oftener than the nose with the great toe.

It is only a step from this view to the acceptance of Bernstein's theory in explanation of the facts of the two-point limen. The present author has gone a little further to present what seems to him a plausible theory of the facts of returning sensitivity after injury to a peripheral nerve, the facts which led Henry Head to posit two classes of tactual sensation, the 'protopathic' and the 'epicritic.' The author still thinks of his own view as plausible and consistent with conservative opinion, but there is no doubt that it has failed to gain favor, because it ventures to make explicit these assumptions that are so often left to implication.

It is only recently that psychologists have come to think of hearing as a spatial sense. However, extensive research upon auditory localization has shown that it possesses some similarities to the other spatial senses, touch and vision. Auditory localization is fully as immediate as tactual, and is often, like the tactual, effected in terms of visual con-textual images. Its primary dimension is left and right, the dimension determined by the position of the two ears. The skin, a surface, can be differentially stimulated at any of a very large number of points, but there are only two points of reception for hearing. One localizes in accordance with the relative effectiveness of stimulation at the two ears, and perceives a sound at the right or the left or at some in-termediate position, as the case may be.

When the ears are stimulated separately and successively, the judgment as to which ear is stimulated first is very ac-curate. A difference almost as small as 0.002 sec. is discrimi-nated correctly as to the ear of prior stimulation. There can be little doubt that there is spatial differentiation at the center in the projection of the paths that lead from the two ears (after some of the auditory fibers have crossed in the brain). The present author has remarked that the facts of localization would follow if the regions of projection for the two ears were adjacent, and if Bernstein's theory applied for the intermediate localizations. Again it is true that conservative psychologists have feared to venture so far; nevertheless this view is still approximately consistent with the facts and has gained, at least temporarily, support from the research of Wever and Bray.

Perhaps the situation with respect to these theories is about as satisfactory as could be expected under the dominance of a faulty dualism. The psychologist has usually posited three terms: (1) peripheral stimulation, (2) central excitation, (3) conscious perceptual datum. Observation yields correlations between (1) and (3). The middle term, (2), has not yet surrendered to any available observational method. Why then has the psychologist tried to make a plausible guess about the nature of central excitation? Because the nature of the relationship between body and mind in a dualistic universe is inscrutable and therefore repugnant to a scientist. If one can minimize this mysterious relationship by reducing it to simple correspondence between (2) and (3) and then undertake to explicate the whole physical system in which (2) follows upon (1), one finds himself with the least objectionable dualistic system. Nevertheless there is an objection to speculating too much about the inaccessible (2), and the psychologist seems in general to have compromised by accepting these theories of projection and correspondence surreptitiously and even unknown to himself.

We have examined the nature of the evidence for these theories. They are not made up out of whole cloth. In their most general forms they are plausible and sometimes probable inferences. Tradition supports them, and thus we needed to examine tradition critically in order to understand the inconsistencies of modern opinion. Now we can turn to the theory of correspondence as our primary concern in the present chapter.

Psychophysiological Correspondence

The principle of psychophysiological correspondence has been recently formulated by Köhler: ". . . *all experienced order in space is a true representation of a corresponding order in the underlying dynamical context of physiological processes.*" Köhler is, of course, not saying here that, when we see a circle, there is somewhere a circular excitation in the brain. He is saying that we may expect a gross correspondence of ordered relationships and that the one totality will resemble the other in its topographic structure.

We have just seen how this theory of correspondence has got itself introduced into psychology and some of the grounds for it. The principal ground would seem to lie in the fact that perception is surprisingly accurate. Illusion and error are, after all, exceptional. This fact once led to the belief that the 'properties' of objects are conducted by the nerves to the mind. Now we might say that the fact gives rise to a 'constancy hypothesis,' at least in the case of extensity, for the perceptual pattern resembles the pattern of the stimulus, and, with the two end terms resembling each other, it seems highly improbable that the middle term, the central excitation, should not also partake of the same resemblance.

At this point we must pause to clarify the relation of our view to the well-known tenets of Gestalt psychology. Gestalt psychologists have objected to a 'constancy hypothesis' of the relation between the stimulus and the phenomenal perception. In the sense in which they have raised the objection they are right. Although there is apt to be a resemblance between stimulation and perception in respect of spatial pattern, the resemblance is not a simple duplication, and experimentation is needed in order to affirm or correct the hypothesis. Nevertheless there is a paradox here that we must fully understand. The 'constancy hypothesis' holds as a general tendency, but the experimental psychology of perception exists solely because this constancy relation is inexact so that the precise dynamics of perceptual structure require investigation. In the case of the relation of central nervous events to introspective phenomena it is Köhler, a Gestalt psychologist, who invokes the 'constancy hypothesis' in the formula quoted above. Here, too, we may suppose that constancy is the fact in the gross, and that experimentation (and a method for such experimentation!) is needed before we can say that *resemblance* means *exact correspondence*.

We must not blame Gestalt psychology if it has seemed to find constancy in the psychophysiological relation between brain and phenomenon, and inconstancy in the psychophysical relation between stimulus and phenomenon. It seems in each case to have stressed the aspect that psychology most needed at the time. However, there is in Gestalt psychology a much more serious source of confusion; the Gestalt psychologists appear to hold to a conventional dualism. Köhler has dealt with electrical fields in the brain as the correlates of conscious phenomena (1920) and formulates this law of resemblance between the "experienced" and the "physiological" orders (1929). Koffka urges that phenomenal visual space is truly three-dimensional and it may, therefore, be correlated with physiological processes of three dimensions in the brain substance (1930). And yet, at least in the present author's opinion, dualism is Gestalt psychology's worst enemy. A Gestalt is a dynamical whole. It is not a mere congeries of parts. A Gestalt cannot include such disparate entities as mind and body. The mysterious mind-body relation admits of no dynamical laws. Köhler's notion of psychophysiological correspondence can mean nothing more intimate than an 'and-connection' (*Und-Verbindung*), at which Wertheimer once so convincingly sniffed.

Let us, therefore, try to restate Köhler's principle with the avoidance of dualistic implications—'outgestalting' Gestalt psychology, as it were. The spatial pattern of stimulation at the periphery is preserved in the brain, not without distortion nor without loss of some characteristics, but in such a way that the spatial order of excitation in the brain is essentially a specific function of the spatial order at the periphery. To this extent we may accept the theory of projection. There need be, however, no fixed central field of projection. The peripheral stimulation initiates a dynamical system of neural discharges which is finally expended in some way that need not for the moment concern us. No stage of this composite system of discharges can very well be called a field of projection. Nevertheless it must be true that there is some stage in the course of this system within the brain where some other neural system or a single pathway can be activated *by* the spatial properties of the first system. Here we face the crucial condition of an awareness of spatial pattern. The activation of some such secondary system must be specifically conditioned upon the spatial relations of the first system which results directly from stimulation. It is this secondary system, specifically representative of the primary spatial relations, that is the ground for the awareness of spatial arrangement. The 'seat of consciousness' can only be the region of this crucial selective response of the secondary system to the spatial character of the first.

There remains, of course, much more to be said on the general problem. Just how, it may be asked, does the relationship between such neural systems come to be the fundamental condition of consciousness? The answer to this question we must defer until chapter 8 (pp. 229-233).

Extension

One needs to distinguish between the awareness of extension and the perception of space. It is these sensory data which vary in the dimension of extensity that are capable of being worked up into adequate perceptions of space. This distinction is well sponsored. Titchener, for instance, was a nativist in his recognition of the sensory 'attribute of extent,' and a geneticist when he came to show how spatial perceptions were built up from attributive extensity. On the other hand, the distinction does not seem to be of great importance in so highly developed a spatial sense as vision, for to be aware of visual extension is somehow to perceive visual space, at least to realize form or formlessness and something of position. But, when we ask whether tones or smells may not have a volumic extension that is not always involved in any specific spatial reference, we begin to see ground for Titchener's meticulosity.

Vision is the most obviously extensional sense. No doubt exists about the primary fact nor about the further fact that extension gets itself organized in at least two dimensions, as an areal spread. The weight of tradition is against the contention that visual extension is volumic or three-dimensional, but it seems probable that the weight of tradition is wrong. We shall find this point illumined in the next section by Koffka's discussion.

In the brain visual extension must be represented by excitatory extension or the multiplicity of excited paths, and the awareness of visual extension would mean a secondary neural system conditioned for its response upon the spatial characteristics of the first. Such is the most conservative general statement. Köhler has pictured what would go on in electrostatic fields suffering little constraint from insula-

tion of the nerve-fibers. Traditional physiology permits a
similar view which is less picturesque. The total spread may
be thought of as distributed over many fibers, and it exists
as a unitary Gestalt only as it functions as a totality for
setting up a specific response or other specific context. This
latter view goes further than Köhler's because it tells how
we come to know about the existence of visual extension.
There is also a compromise view. It is the one which supposes that the central excitation is confined to fiber-paths,
but notes that the elaborate branching of the axons and
dendrites of many neurons in the central nervous system
practically creates a reticulum in which Köhler's fields might
be approximated.

Is touch also an extensional sense? Tradition is affirma-
tive and positive on this point, and there seems to be no
convincing reason for contradicting tradition. The phenomena of tactual excitation must be similar to the visual.

However, the case of touch is less obvious to ordinary
introspection than is the case of vision. Most persons surrogate for tactual space with visual imagery. One asks of
himself the question: Has this touch simple extension?
He finds that he visualizes the spread of the touch upon
the skin and returns an answer based upon the visual
substitute. However, there is evidence from congenitally
blind persons and from those rare laboratory observers
who lack almost all visual imagery that tactual space can
support itself without dependence upon vision.

Perhaps the extensional nature of vision is emphasized
by the fact that the entire visual field is always excited in
visual perception. Even black is a 'sensation,' so that no
visual sensory datum ever arises except as a spatial differentiation from the rest of the field. Although under attention we can become conscious of almost any specific
region of the skin—a toe, a finger-tip, or the end of the

nose—it is clear that a tactual sensation is not fitted into a tactual field in a manner analogous to the case in vision. Consciously one does not live within a continuous tactual 'bag of skin'; the conscious 'skin' is very patchy, with a forearm, perhaps, completely missing here, a knee and a shin gone there, and an elbow presently turning up close to a shoulder.

We are faced next with the problem of auditory extension. Are tones volumic? We have already seen in chapter 2 (pp. 29f.) that there is a dispute as to the correct answer to this question, and we must examine the case with great care.

Tradition is against the belief in the extension of tones. Touch and vision are the spatial senses; hearing is not spatial. However, there lies in this denial of spatiality in hearing a ground for admitting the possibility of bare extension. Nobody has ever argued that tones have form or shape. What they have is position and size. Having position, they can move; but, having size, they do not, as one might expect, have any definite or significant shape. However, to lack shape is not necessarily to lack extension, *i.e.*, the beginnings of spatiality before there is even enough form to show whether the tones should be regarded as areal or solid. It may be that tones actually furnish us with an example of primitive, prespatial extension.

The more sophisticated objectors to the doctrine of tonal extension have generally admitted the fact that observers can render consistent judgments of the 'size' or 'volume' of tones, and have argued that the judgments depend upon 'association.' Some of these objectors say that low tones are large because they are known to be produced by large objects or instruments, and that high tones come from small stimulus-objects. This objection is, however, too vague to be telling. Unless it has to do merely with the genesis of the judgments, it can be answered by the appeal to introspection: the observers are making judgments of tones and not of associated objects. On the other hand, this very introspection reveals the fact that the great majority of observers speak a little loosely when they say that the judgments are "of the tones." Usually the judgments refer directly to visual surrogates of the tones; the observer has visual imagery representing the tones and describes their extensive characteristics. A high tone may be "small, bright, blue and solid," and a low tone "large, dark, brownish and gaseous." Is it not possible that the tone never had extension of its own and that it gained extension merely because it was represented by a visual image?

Well, it is possible, but it is by no means necessary. Spatial judgments of tactual impressions are almost always mediated by visual imagery and yet extension is not denied to touch. We do not have for this problem of tonal extension evidence from congenitally blind persons as we do for touch, but the visual surrogation is so similar in the two cases that the presumption of its irrelevance in both cases is strong. The author knows of direct observation that bears out this point. S. W. Fernberger, who has very little visual imagery indeed, was one of Halverson's observers in preliminary experiments on the localization of tones, experiments in which all the other observers described the localization (and later the size) of visual images representing the tones in the spatial field. Fernberger gave results comparable with the others in immediacy and the nature of the function derived from them, but he had no visual imagery for the tones. He said: "I point with my horn," meaning that he indicated the localization to himself in kinesthetic terms as if he were pointing with a horn on the forehead. This is just what happens with touch; the visual surrogates function for the tactual data until the visual surrogates are prevented; then they turn out to be non-essential.

All these indirect arguments, however, will be of little

importance in comparison with the verdict of experimental observation when the necessary body of experimentation becomes available. The brief history of the experimental research is as follows.

Stumpf and others had observed that high tones are small and low tones large. Titchener claimed for tonal volume the status of an attribute and guessed from casual observation as to the nature of the quantitative functional relation between perceived volume and the frequency of the stimulus. Rich was the first person actually to experiment. He used the tones of Stern variators and found that his observers had no difficulty at all in saying which of two tones of different pitch was the larger, nor in remaining quantitatively consistent in the making of such judgments. He determined six differential thresholds at intervals between 100 and 6,400 cycles, and found that the threshold is approximately a constant proportion (between 3 per cent and 4 per cent) of the frequency at which it is determined, that is to say, it varies logarithmically with frequency in the way that musical interval varies. The thresholds for pitch show no such simple logarithmic relationship to the frequency, and besides they are much smaller than the volumic thresholds. For instance the threshold for pitch near middle *c* may be a single cycle or less, whereas the threshold that Rich found for volume is about 12 cycles, which is a musical *comma* or the fifth of a musical semi-tone.

There has been somewhat of a puzzle as to why pitch and volume should be covariants with frequency. It would seem more probable, in view of what we know about visual and tactual dispersion, that volume and intensity should vary together—an hypothesis that Halverson undertook to test experimentally. Halverson accustomed his observers to make judgments of volumic differences when the frequency of the tonal stimulus was varied, and then asked for the same kind of judgments when the frequency was kept constant and the energy of the stimulus varied. The observers reported volumic differences under the new conditions, and

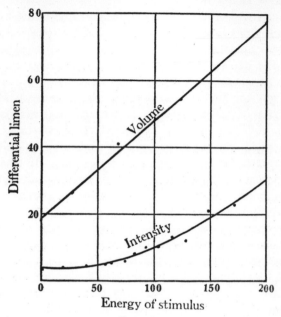

FIG. 11

RELATION OF TONAL VOLUME AND INTENSITY TO THE ENERGY OF THE STIMULUS

Halverson's data. The differential limens for volume and the differential limens for intensity are different functions of the energy of the stimulus and different amounts for any given value of the stimulus. The energy of the tone was varied by changing the resistance in a telephone circuit; hence the scale of the figures is arbitrary, numbers taken from the scale of the rheostat.

Halverson determined the volumic thresholds and also the thresholds for intensity at various energies for a tone of 1,000 cycles. Fig. 11 shows his results. The thresholds for volume turned out to be much larger than the thresholds for intensity, and the shape of the functions was different in the two cases. Thus tonal volume seemed to be established as a covariant with intensity and a datum separate from intensity.

It is not impossible to see consistency in these two results. In the experiment on volume and intensity, pitch was kept constant, and it would seem that tonal volume must therefore, like intensity, depend upon the energy or the amplitude of the stimulus. In the experiment upon volume and pitch, it was not possible to keep intensity constant because there is no certain way of equating the intensities of two different pitches. The situation is much more complicated than seems possible at first thought. If both Halverson's and Rich's results are correct, volume cannot be dependent upon the frequency of the stimulus, but it may depend upon energy or amplitude or some related variable. If two tonal stimuli have the same energy and different frequencies, the tone of greater frequency has the lesser amplitude. Rich's stimuli were uncontrolled in energy, but, if they were approximately equal in energy, then their amplitudes would have been very different. And there are other constants of a tonal stimulus besides frequency, amplitude, and energy to which appeal might be made.

It would seem that these experiments of Halverson's and Rich's ought to be conclusive. Nevertheless the volumic judgments have proved difficult and the matter is not settled one way or the other. F. A. Pattie attempted to vary both frequency and intensity at the same time so as to equate volume; a faint low pitch might be made the same size as a loud high pitch. Pattie found that such heterophonic judgments were very difficult and unreliable. He did not publish the results. P. M. Zoll, working in coöperation with the author, has found the utmost difficulty in duplicating Rich's and Halverson's thresholds. Gundlach has raised objections to the simple sensory status of tonal volume, and Gundlach and Bentley have failed to distinguish volumic thresholds from thresholds for tonal "brightness" or even from the thresholds for pitch. It is evident that we must await still more research.

Before we leave this topic it is perhaps interesting to ask whether there are any physiological grounds for expecting to find extensity among tones. The organ of Corti is an extended organ like the skin and the retina; it ought to furnish a field of excitation capable of becoming the ground of perceived extension. However, for auditory extension to become conscious, it would presumably also be necessary for this excitatory field to be stimulated differentially in respect of space. One could not become aware even of bare extension unless it varied in amount. In spite of the controversies about the operation of the cochlea in hearing, most theories assume that the spread of excitation would vary with the energy of the stimulation; some think that the spread would be from the base of the cochlea up as the amplitude of excitation increases; others think that the spread would be around some central resonating point of excitation. All in all, then, it would seem rather surprising than otherwise if we were not able to perceive a bare extensity attaching to tones, although the perception would have so little practical use that we should not expect it to be realized frequently without the particular pressure of a laboratory instruction.

There remains, of course, the question of extension for taste and for smell. There are no data, but it seems reasonable to suppose that taste must be like touch, and that our inability to answer the question at once is due to the fact that gustatory spatial patterns are almost always accompanied by tactual patterns. Certainly, however, one perceives vaguely gustatory forms when different sapid substances diffuse irregularly in water that fills the mouth.

On the other hand, it is not so clear that we ought to expect extension in smells. The organ does not present a large surface, and the different parts of it cannot be differentially stimulated in respect of space. Observers can judge olfactory sensations as of different volumes, but the experimenter who made this observation was not sufficiently confident of the meaning of the results to publish them.

We may summarize this section by saying that visual sensation is organized in the extensive dimension and so highly organized that extension practically always appears as form and localization. Tactual sensation, although often supported by visual surrogates, is the second spatial sense, less precisely organized than vision. Little is known of taste, but it is probably like touch. Auditory extension is not accepted by the majority of psychologists as a fact, and yet there is some definite experimental evidence for its existence. It presents a problem that can be settled by further research. Of olfactory extension nothing is known, and it is not even clear that the physiology of excitation is such that extensive organization ought to result.

The Visual Third Dimension

Sensory extension does not in itself imply spatial dimensionality. It is conventional to think of visual and tactual extension as areal, partly because the retina and the skin are surfaces and stimulation takes place in areal fields in the sense-organ, and partly because a projection theory implies that the spatial relations at the periphery are represented by a spatial pattern in the cross-section of the afferent conduction. Even such primitive dimensionality involves, however, a simple kind of organization of sensory material into a form, which is perhaps not to be regarded as implicit in bare sensory extension. The point is not important at this level of discussion. Obviously visual and tactual perceptions are always organized at least into areal extension. Sensation in either of these sense-departments never occurs without extension in at least two dimensions. However, the matter becomes more important when we come to consider the status of the third visual dimension. If the first two dimensions of vision already imply a certain degree of formal organization, we shall certainly expect the third dimension to be understood only in relation to the structure of form.

In the case of tones extension has been supposed to be volumic. Tonal volume, however, furnishes us with an example of unformed extension rather than of a literally three-dimensional volume. The ear does not function as a surface upon which a stimulating field can be projected, and there is no immediate pressure therefore to regard tones, when they seem to differ in size, as areal. The term volume connotes a lack of form as compared with the constraints of limitation to a surface or a line.

A very special problem appears, however, in connection with the third visual dimension. Let us first understand clearly the view of the older introspective psychology about this matter.

The traditional view—the view of Wundt and the geneticists in spatial theories—held that visual space is, at the primary level of organization, two-dimensional, and that the third dimension arises only out of further complication. There are three possible kinds of such complication.

(1) In the first place, the perception of distance may be dependent upon the convergence of the two eyes or the accommodation of the lenses of the eyes, that is to say, we may discriminate differences in the distances of visual objects because specific degrees of convergence and accommodation are required for the different distances and thus come to 'mean' those distances. But how do convergences

and accommodations affect the perception? This question has not always been specifically answered, but the most explicit reply—a view consonant with Titchener's context theory of perception—is that convergence and accommodation are sensed, and that the kinesthetic sensations of convergence and accommodation supplement the visual core of the perception, indicating the distances of the seen objects. Thus distance would be a 'meaning' added to a visual core by an appropriate kinesthetic context.

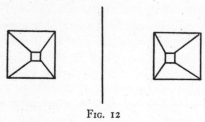

FIG. 12

STEREOGRAM OF TRUNCATED PYRAMID

When such a card in a stereoscope has the left drawing shown to the left eye and the right drawing to the right eye, the observer sees the pyramid solid and convex toward himself. If the card is cut in half and the two halves interchanged for the two eyes, then the perspective reverses and the perception is as if the observer were looking inside a hollow pyramid or were looking down a corridor.

(2) The visual perception of solidity often arises as the result of the disparity between the retinal images, a disparity caused by parallax of the two eyes. The stereoscope is the instrument that demonstrates the effectiveness of this factor. Fig. 12 represents a simple geometrical stereogram. If the image at the right is projected upon the retina of the right eye, and the left image upon the left retina, and the two are allowed to coincide—the stereoscope effects this result optically—then one may see a truncated pyramid extending far out convexly toward himself. And this perception results because (we say) the images provided for the two sides

. are like those which would naturally come to the two eyes
with the difference that parallax would give to a pyramid
thus convex toward the observer. If Fig. 12 is cut in half
and the halves interchanged for the two eyes, then one
sees the same geometrical form concave, as if he were looking down a long corridor; and the explanation in terms of
parallax is the same as before. Since for the two eyes there
is but a single field of vision, it is natural to suppose that
the solid figure results simply from the superposition of the
two images. However, the contemplation of Fig. 12 shows
that the two figures cannot exactly be superimposed; if
the bases coincide, the tops are double; if the tops coincide,
the bases are double. Sometimes in viewing such a diagram
through the stereoscope this persistent doubleness of one
part or the other of the figure is introspectively apparent.
There can be no doubt that it is this *potential* disparity that
is the ground of the perception of solidity. While such a
situation is not readily subsumed under the context theory
of perception, the naïve old-fashioned view was that the
retinal disparity came to 'mean' solidity, as if the disparity
were seen but the idea of solidity were all that got into
knowledge. Perhaps no one has ever quite reached this level
of naïveté; certainly Titchener believed that the disparate
fields managed to fuse in some inexplicable way; but the
preceding sentence expresses the natural trend for a projection theory of areal visual space when it comes to the
problem of perceived solidity.

(3) Of course there are also the secondary criteria, as
they are called, of visual distance and solidity: linear perspective, light and shade, and all the other factors that can
give depth in a picture. However, of these criteria there
seems never to have been any theory at all, except the vague
associationistical one that they have come through past
experience to 'mean' depth.

It is easy to expose the weaknesses of these traditional views and even to caricature them, but it is very much more difficult to displace the ignorance upon which they are based. However, there is one constructive theory, one to which Koffka has recently lent the weight of his opinion. It may be—so the new view runs—that the visual perception of space involves a three-dimensional neural pattern in the brain. Let us see how good an argument we can make for this view.

We may begin with the case of the stereoscopic perception of Fig. 12. We can distinguish consciously between different parts of the field of vision, but we cannot distinguish excitation of one retina from excitation of the other. The obvious conclusion is that the two fields of excitation fuse with each other in a point-to-point correspondence. This is the old theory of corresponding points and of projection. It leads to the conclusion that the doubling of the combined images *is,* in some way, the solidity. Such a notion, however, involves an inconsistency. The theory of corresponding points is based upon the evidence of introspection, and we ought therefore to accept as equally valid the introspective evidence about solidity. Introspection shows that, although sometimes the disparity of images is seen in stereoscopic observation, ordinarily the perception of solidity is as truly tridimensional as the perception of a surface is areal, and that perceived disparity is not normal to stereoscopic solidification. How can these things be?

Plainly it is impossible to superimpose the two halves of Fig. 12 without disparity between either the large squares or the small squares. If both the large squares and the small squares combine at the same time—and introspection indicates that they may—then the fusions cannot be due to the movements of the eyes and the consequent movements of the images upon the retinas; they must therefore involve some relative shift of excitation within the central nervous system. Let us suppose that the drawings of Fig. 12 are presented in a stereoscope to an observer and that, for the first few moments, the disparity remains apparent in the perception, with the two large squares fusing into one and the two small squares overlapping inside. Presently the small squares pull together and fuse without the large square's being resolved into its components, and at the same time the figure stretches itself out in the third dimension. The simultaneous fusion of both the large and the small squares occurs only when they appear in different planes, and it is natural for us to transfer this phenomenon of perception to the neural pattern as we have been accustomed to do in accordance with the theory of correspondence or, in respect of bidimensional patterns, the theory of projection.

The readiness with which areal patterns, binocularly perceived, may become tridimensional has been shown by experiments with optical illusions. Most of these illusions consist of a primary stimulus-pattern which is distorted in perception by the addition of a secondary stimulus-pattern. For instance, in the Zöllner illusion the primary stimulus is a set of parallel lines, and the secondary stimulus consists of little cross-bars that cross the odd lines in one direction and the even lines in another. This secondary stimulus distorts the primary so that the lines no longer appear parallel. It is a very obvious experiment to try physiologically to localize this effect of the secondary stimulus upon the primary by presenting the primary stimulus to only one eye and the secondary stimulus to the other eye. The experiment is easy with the use of the stereoscope. If the illusion persists, the interaction of the stimuli must be in the central nervous system; if the illusion fails, it might lie in the retina. However, the experiment brings a surprising result. The illusion neither succeeds nor fails, but the pattern extends itself into the third dimension, with the odd lines lying in a different plane from the even lines. Thus we see how easily visual organization passes into a third dimension.

As soon as we understand the necessity for the tridimensional organization of visual perception, we can begin to see significance in the tridimensionalities that appear immediately in introspection. When the pyramid of Fig. 12 is seen as solid in the stereoscope, one actually sees the bound-

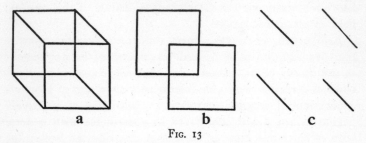

a   b   c

FIG. 13

REVERSIBLE PERSPECTIVE IN THE NECKER CUBE

In *a* one sees a cube. With continued scrutiny the perspective of the cube may reverse, but the figure remains always a cube. It cannot be seen as a flat diagram in the plane of the paper. However, both *b* and *c* can easily be seen as flat diagrams. Yet *b* and *c* added together give *a*. The problem is to see *a* simply as the simultaneous presentation of *b* and *c* without the perception of solidity. After Koffka.

ing surfaces of the solid as transparent planes through which the black lines are visible. This "glassy sensation" is well known to psychologists and has been the subject of some observational study.

It is equally obvious that visual tridimensionality does not necessarily depend upon retinal disparity even though the more striking illusions of depth are stereoscopic. The cube in Fig. 13a is irresistibly a cube. As one examines it, its perspective reverses so that the far surface becomes the near and one sees the bottom of the base instead of the top of the base. But, reversed, it is still a solid figure. It is practically impossible to see the figure as the plane pattern of black lines on a white surface which it 'really' is. Figs. 13b and 13c can easily be seen as plane patterns, but it comes as something of a shock to discover that the combination of these two plane figures will give the solid Fig. 13a. The reader who tries to see Fig. 13a as a plane combination of Figs. 13b and 13c will appreciate how insistently tridimensional Fig. 13a is. It is on such illustrations that Koffka bases his argument for the tridimensionality of the cerebral field of visual excitation.

Koffka can, of course, accept this conclusion more easily than we. He and other Gestalt psychologists do not believe in the theory of projection; they do believe in psychophysiological correspondence, and ordinarily they accept Köhler's conception of central excitation as consisting of relatively unconstrained fields, configured in accordance with general laws of the same kind as those that describe the patterning of electrical charges within a conducting medium. The figure in perspective can be regarded as arousing a tridimensional excitation because of internal stresses that are relieved in a certain symmetrical form. Stereoscopic solidity occurs because certain parts tend naturally to fuse and in fusing eject themselves from other parts. The cerebral dynamics is not worked out, of course; we are still quite uncertain that this sort of freedom exists within the brain.

However, it is very doubtful whether we need to accept the extreme constraints of traditional physiology and to regard the central nervous system as consisting of insulated neurons, conducting impulses which converge at synapses upon other neurons or which diverge from them. The simplest facts of stereoscopy seem to require more freedom than conventional physiology has allowed.

Thus we are faced with a dilemma between two opposite hypotheses about the action of the brain. We have the principles of dynamic organization of Gestalt psychology on the one hand, and we have the systems of reflex arcs of conventional physiology on the other. There are such good grounds for both views that it rather seems as if some sort of compromise were likely to be discovered. In this connection we must remember that the elaborately branched axons and dendrites in the brain may give it more the character of a network than of a system of chains, and it is not at all impossible that the well-recognized principles of nerve-conduction, worked out for peripheral nerve-fibers, might apply strictly here, and yet the impulses, because of the branching of the neurons, might seem to exhibit great freedom of organization. A speculative example of how the strict binocular projection of a stereogram might result in a tridimensional field of excitation, one that would reverse if the retinal disparity were reversed, is given in the notes to this chapter (pp. 118f.).

Size

For convenience we may distinguish the problem of size from the problems of extension and of form. *Extension* is primary; we say what are the sensory phenomena which vary spatially and which may thus become organized in the dimension of extensity. *Size* is, as it were, the amount of extension. *Form* is the organization of the sensory material in respect of extensity.

If size is the amount of extension, it is plain that its meaning will usually be relativistic. A sensory impression is small in respect of another that is larger, and large in respect of a smaller. Even in the judgments of everyday life our estimates of size in the external world are fairly accurate only because there are always in the world of observation so many known sizes which may serve as standards of comparison. In the psychological laboratory experiments upon

size almost invariably require a comparison between two
sizes. In fact it is difficult to give a meaning to the notion
of absolute size, as it seems to occur, for example, in the
illusion of the difference in size of the moon on the horizon
and at the zenith.

Thus it appears that, in the great majority of cases, the
perception of size consists of the discrimination of relative
sizes. If we wish to translate this statement into physiological terms, we can only say that two parts of a system of
excitation must differ in extension and that the nervous
system must respond differentially to these differentiated extensions. Such a conception is very difficult to reconcile with
the traditional neuron theory of the central nervous system.
It requires that some simple and presumably narrowly localized system of excitation be set up as the essential consequence of a differential within a large and widespread system. Any theory of space perception must, however, in this
sense involve a physiological 'convergence'; a spatial field,
involving various differentiations, must be reduced in its
consequents to some simple judgment. Only a complex
physiological theory will explain how a man can correctly
and immediately point to the larger of two objects.

However, the instances of the perception of 'absolute size'
throw more light on the matter. In strict logic *size* has
meaning only relativistically; nevertheless size may be 'absolute' psychologically when the perception includes no conscious comparison. The illusion involved in the size of the
moon is the most striking example. At the zenith the moon
appears to be of a given size, and most persons accept this
size as the 'natural' size of the moon, although they may
differ greatly in comparing it with familiar objects. On the
horizon the moon is gigantic. This illusion has been discussed
since antiquity. It seems not to be due to comparison of the
horizon-moon with visible objects on the earth's surface.

Rather does it seem to be dependent upon the position of the head and eyes in viewing the moon, as if the posture for upward gaze 'shrank' the lunar image. However, the illusion seems also to depend in part upon the indeterminate distance of the moon, for it is diminished if the moon be projected upon a near surface. Thus Helmholtz's test of projecting the horizon-moon to the zenith and the zenith-moon to the horizon by means of a mirror is apt to fail because the surface of the mirror (or reflecting prism) remains visible. Schur, in one of the most recent experimental studies, has shown that the illusion is measurable with cardboard discs at distances under 33 m., that it is greater at the greater distances, and that at 33 m. the 'horizon' image may be almost twice as large as the one at the 'zenith.' Thus the evidence indicates that size and distance are closely related and that they tend to be codeterminate.

Size and distance are codeterminate because size is most definitely determined when distance is most determinate. Distance is most accurately determinate for short distances, and there the illusion of the horizon and the zenith is least. Size 'stays put.' The illusion increases for the greater and less determinate distances. The illusion then would be maximal in the case of the moon where distance is entirely indeterminate. It may be, as Zoth and Schur have suggested, that the raising of the head and eyes to view the zenith 'drains' the lunar image, causing an actual shrinkage in the size of the excitatory field upon which the judgment depends. Nevertheless size is free to vary in this way only when, or in as far as, distance is indeterminate.

We know on other grounds that perceived size is strictly dependent upon perceived distance and the size of the retinal image. As a perceived object recedes from an observer, the linear size of the retinal image decreases in proportion to the distance of the object from the eye. The perceived size does not decrease so rapidly as the size of the retinal image, nor does it remain unchanged. The size changes in accordance with a definite function which has been made out in the "alley experiments," experiments in which various near extents are successively equated to a fixed remote extent, as if one were defining the loci of the walls of an alley so that the two side-walls, as one looks down the alley, shall be everywhere equidistant.

Now we can see what a vague thing size is. Most judgments of size are relative and not absolute. Visual size does not depend wholly upon the visual angle of the retinal image; when two objects vary in distance, size depends on the distance in an exactly measurable (but otherwise unpredictable) way. As distance becomes great and therefore indeterminate, other factors, such as the position of the head and eyes in viewing the zenith, may enter in to influence size. We may still believe that perceived size depends upon the magnitude of a central field of excitation, but we cannot maintain any simple theory of projection.

The illusion of the moon indicates that there is some meaning to the notion of 'absolute size,' but it is very difficult to find other examples. It is easier to make the negative assertion and to say that ordinarily we are quite unaware of the absolute size of sensory impressions. For instance, it is impossible to be sure that size does not vary with attention. It is said that a half-page of magazine advertising is more effective than a quarter-page, but that the half of a large page is no more effective than the half of a small page. Who shall say that the large half-page, when the page is the field of attention, is any larger in perception than the small half-page? Let us try this experiment. Hold a pencil vertically at arm's length. Note the breadth of the pencil. Halve the distance of the pencil from the eyes, so that the retinal image becomes twice as broad. We do not expect the perceived breadth to double, but can you be sure that it has at all increased in size? Now hold the pencil again at arm's length, and concentrate the attention upon it, noticing every possible detail in the texture of its surface. Then extend the attention over the field of vision as widely as possible so that the pencil becomes merely a small object in the midst of the field. Does the pencil change in perceived size as the attention shifts? Again it is almost impossible to say. For the author the perceived change in size is somewhat greater in the case of the attentional shift than in the case of the change of distance; but the point is, in any case, that the judgment is difficult and at best uncertain. Absolute size is not easily perceived.

In this connection we may anticipate the mention of Lashley's experiments in the next section. Lashley interprets his experiments upon the cerebral cortex as meaning that, within certain limits, any part of the cortex can perform any cortical function ("equipotentiality"), but that the more highly intelligent or discriminative functions require a larger part of the cortex ("mass action"), although *any* large part is equally useful. This view of cortical function is more compatible with the facts of the perception of size than is any simple projection theory. It also suggests how size, when not otherwise controlled, might vary with attention. We know, for example, that discrimination of fine details within a small region is possible only under concentrated attention. Perhaps, however, the attention is not really narrowed to the object, but the object is perceptually expanded to the attention (and hence to the cortex), thus making spatial discrimination (spatially differentiated reaction) easier. (Cf. pp. 101-104.) At any rate the psychological fact of the limited range of apprehension must somehow enter into any physiological theory of perception.

Form

The most significant thing about the perception of form is its immediacy. Visual experience seems to come formed. So also does tactual experience, if one makes allowance for the absence of sharp tactual contours. Consider the visual perception of a square. The old school of the form-quality held that the four lines are the elements of the square, and that, given these elements and the relations between them, the square is 'founded' as a secondary or derived 'form-quality.' This view has become nonsensical because no sensible meaning can be given to the fact of 'founding.' We have no reason at all to believe that the lines are psychologically prior to the square and that the square is founded upon them. The square is 'there' as immediately as the lines. The square is a perceived form and not a sum of four perceived lines, just as much as a line is a perceived form and not 'a row of sensations' (as the older psychology used to imply).

At first thought it seems as if a modified projection theory held the key to the problem of perceived form. Usually the form of the stimulus, imaged upon the retina—so the theory would run—is projected, at least approximately, upon the brain, when, because of psychophysiological correspondence, we perceive the form. Square stimulus—square retinal image —square central excitation—square perception—such is the norm. However (the theory would continue), the optical illusions exhibit a number of ways in which dynamic principles of organization establish deviations from this norm, and we can assume that the dynamics are physiological, that the deviations are cerebral, and that psychophysiological correspondence is as direct as ever for the illusory perception. Such would be a dynamical projection theory, in which projection of form is a central tendency and a constancy hypothesis fails only because of dynamical principles of organization that create deviations from the central tendency.

Of two difficulties with such a theory the lesser is that it is, in reality, only an incomplete theory. Suppose that we were to admit the physiological view in the preceding paragraph. A retinal square becomes a brain square by projection. Very well, how do we know about the square? How does this series of events come to terminate in adequate perception? The physiology of introspection must constitute one-half of the problem of perception. If we believe in projection and thus in the conduction of nerve-impulses along relatively insulated fibers, we have to say how, in the brain, the projected pattern comes to lead to so simple a discriminatory end-product as the introspective judgment. A very simple introspection is one in which the observer raises his finger for a perceived square and does nothing for any other perceived form. The final physiological theory of the perception of form will have to show how a square will excite this final common path, while a rhombus with angles of 85° and 95° will not.

However, the greatest of our troubles is not the failure to be able to explain the condensation of an actual excitatory form to the simpler physiology of a judgment that the form is what it is. The perception has turned out to be ever so much more complexly determined than we should have dared to assert a mere decade ago. The evidence for complication comes to some extent from psychopathology, but most particularly from Lashley's experiments which we must now consider.

Traditional psychophysiology has accepted, along with the theory of spatial projection, the theory of sensory centers or areas in the cerebral cortex. In fact the notion of sensory centers is quite old, being implicit in Johannes Müller's admission that the specific energies of sensory nerves may reside in the central terminations of these nerves (1838). Broca's supposed discovery of a speech center came somewhat later (1861), and then Fritsch and Hitzig described motor centers in the region of the cortex in front of the fissure of Rolando. Afterwards the area back of this fissure came to be regarded as a region functioning for somesthetic sensations; the auditory center was assigned to the temporal lobe; and vision, on more reliable evidence than was available for the other senses, was localized in the occipital cortex.

Fig. 14 shows for the rat the modern topographical view. The nine lettered areas, shown for the dorsal and lateral aspects of the rat's cortex, are areas distinguished by Fortuyn on the anatomical grounds of difference in arrangement of the half dozen laminations of the cells in the cortex. The letters are Fortuyn's and we shall presently have a great deal to say about area w in the visual cortex. The right half of the dorsal aspect of the cortex in Fig. 14 shows the functions that can be most satisfactorily assigned (in part from analogy with evidence for mammals higher than the rat) to Fortuyn's various areas. For instance, f, f', c and n seem to include all the points from which Lashley got muscular movement from direct stimulation of the cortex. There is a great deal of evidence that visual functions tend to involve the areas w, m' and aa. Presumably j is especially important for somesthesia, p for audition, and k for smell.

However, Fig. 14 distorts the facts. The boundaries between the anatomical regions are not so sharp as the lines of the figure. None of these functions is limited strictly to the corresponding area. All areas seem to participate in some intelligent behavior. There is no persistent finer localization of function within an area. For instance, repeated direct stimulation of a given point within the 'motor' area may continue to give rise to the same movement until an-

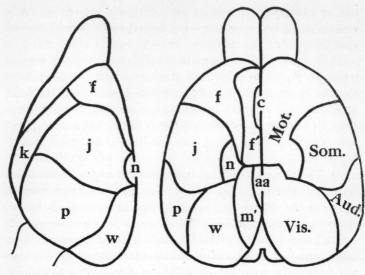

FIG. 14

TOPOGRAPHY OF THE CEREBRAL CORTEX IN THE RAT: FORTUYN'S AREAS

The figure shows the projections of the lateral aspect (one hemisphere) and the dorsal aspect (two hemispheres) of the rat's brain. In the lateral and left dorsal aspects are shown the chief cyto-architectural areas as established by Fortuyn. The letters identifying the areas are Fortuyn's and are used by Lashley and in the present text. The actual shape of the areas is Lashley's modification of Fortuyn. In the right dorsal aspect are shown, in relation to certain groupings of Fortuyn's areas, the more specific functions of these areas, as they have been established in tradition and verified by recent research. The abbreviations refer to the Motor, Somesthetic, Auditory, and Visual areas. The function of area *k* is perhaps olfactory. These correlations are only approximate. Lashley's theory is that all areas are equipotential for higher functions like intelligence, and that different parts of a small area are equipotential with one another for the specific localized functions of the area. See text. Figure adapted from Fortuyn and Lashley.

other point is stimulated. Then the original correlation between point of stimulation and movement no longer holds, although it may recur again after a time. There seem to be normal correlations between points of the cortex and particular movements, for which substitution is very easily made whenever central conditions are disturbed by stimulation of another part of the cortex.

This variability of function of different cortical regions seems to be the general rule. Regions which normally have specific functions also participate in general functions, or under changed central conditions give over their specific functions to other regions. Thus Lashley finds that in intelligent activities all parts of the cortex may be *equipotential*. Learning a maze may be regarded as requiring 'intelligence' in a rat. The capacity to learn a complicated maze is diminished by the destruction of cortical tissue, and the diminution of the capacity varies directly with the amount of tissue destroyed. This is Lashley's law of *mass action:* Intelligence (the kind required for a rat to learn a maze) depends upon the *amount* of cortical tissue available, but not at all upon the particular areas which make up the total amount, for the areas are equipotential, and one is as good as another in making up a sum.

Now let us examine the functioning of area w (Fig. 14), which can be regarded as a visual projection area. The lateral portion of this area seems to be essential for the visual discrimination of patterns (*e.g.,* the discrimination of a given triangle from the same triangle inverted). When the area is destroyed such discriminatory habits are abolished and cannot be reëstablished by training. This fact seems to affirm the visual function of the area. However, area w is also equipotential with all other parts of the cortex for the learning of a maze; take away area w and the acquisition of such a habit is impeded as much as would result from taking away an equal area elsewhere. Area w does not contribute to the learning of a maze only because learning the maze involves vision; blind rats can learn the maze and are more disturbed by the subsequent removal of area w

than normally trained rats are disturbed by blinding the eyes. Area *w*, while specific for the perception of visual patterns, simply contributes to mass action in performance in the maze. In the case of the discrimination of brightness this area has an intermediate effect. Its removal does not abolish the capacity to discriminate brightnesses, but it renders the discrimination less accurate and the differential threshold larger. The acquisition of a habit dependent upon the discrimination of brightnesses is made more difficult by the removal of area *w*, although such acquisition is not retarded in its initial phases. When parts of area *w* act specifically, as in the visual discrimination of forms, these parts have shown no further specificity within themselves; the parts of such an area are equipotential, and incomplete 'insult' to the area interferes with the function as to degree but not specifically as to kind. For instance, incomplete 'insult' of area *w* seems rather to decrease visual acuity than to establish a blind spot in the field of vision.

Obviously the situation which we are considering is extremely complex and interpretation of these experiments must be made with great care. Some of the details of the preceding paragraph may prove to be incorrect. However, the general picture is pretty clear.

In the first place, it is clear that we are in the presence of something like a hierarchy of functions in respect of equipotentiality and specificity of localization. At an upper level is intelligence, as measured by ability to learn a maze. It is dependent upon the mass action of the entire cortex and all parts of the cortex are equipotential in respect of it. Then at a lower and more specific level there is the perception of spatial form. It depends upon mass action of equipotential parts of the lateral portion of area *w*. Insult to any other part of the cortex leaves this function unaffected. Then, presumably at a third level, there is the gross perception of objects and their position, without discrimination of pattern or form. This function depends upon the optic radiations from the internal capsule to the cortex, but persists with the complete destruction of area w. Finally, at the lowest level, there is the visual discrimination of brightnesses, which persists when the optic radiations are interrupted, but would be abolished at some still lower level. This discrimination occurs to the total brightness of a field, for there can be no perception of pattern or even of gross form when the optic radiations are interrupted.

At the periphery and the lower levels we have localization of function. In the cortex we have some localization for certain functions, but in general a lack of specificity. We must look here for dynamical organization of excitation, relatively indifferent as to locus, but dependent upon the amount of excitable tissue available for finer differentiation. The problem as to how such an organization converges upon a common path, which is the introspection of it, is no greater than the problem of how the organization comes about, independent of locus, from an approximately specific projection of peripheral excitation.

The conclusion as to visual form is that its perception depends upon the functioning of a fairly well localized region of the cortex—in the rat the lateral portion of area w. Within this region there seems to be no further specific localization. All parts are equipotential, and acuity and the discrimination of detail depend upon mass action. Presumably partial insult to the area befogs vision, or else, since it reduces the excitable area, it suppresses detail in the same way that detail is eliminated at the periphery by the diminution of the size of a stimulus-object.

There is no reason to suppose that the organization that represents visual form in area w is anything other than a spatial organization. Spatial differentiation exists for form at the periphery and is projected inward. Presumably it retains its dimensional integrity. On the other hand, we have no ground for asserting a simple projection theory. A seen circle is not necessarily a circular excitation. Simplicity of projection is inevitably upset by the fact that the field of vision always involves both hemispheres of the brain, two areas w. Gestalt psychology has shown us that certain forms, like the circle, are natural and that incomplete forms tend toward these natural shapes. From such data we may eventually get some notion of the type of organization of form in the cortex. It is presumably here in area w that there occur the tridimensional forms, required for the perception of depth with disparity and also for the various conditions that give depth monocularly. (See pp. 86-94, 118f.)

Area j (Fig. 14) is historically the somesthetic area, and certain experiments indicate that its insult in the rat leads to temporary disturbance of sensitivity to posture. Presumably then some part of area j corresponds in tactual function with the function of the lateral part of area w for vision. In human beings there is, however, one fundamental difference between visual and tactual form. Visual form, as Rubin has shown, is fundamentally organized with contours, that is to say, boundary lines that differentiate an object of attention from its ground, and which may even separate a figure from its ground in perceptual depth. Area w in man ought to be the seat of this fundamental dichotomizing principle of visual organization. Tactual forms, however, do not show sharp contours; they have blurred "edges" only, as Rubin has also shown. Spatial organization in area j is possibly less sharp, though the cause may be at the periphery where the skin with its tensions and deformations would tend to blur contours into "edges."

It may be observed that we come here upon a datum as to the relative primacy of the conscious dimensions. It has been asked: Is quality prior to extensity or can space just as easily be primary? Can the *same* square in phenomenal experience be both cold and red? Apparently modal differences in quality are physiologically prior to form. If a square is both seen and felt, there must be first in excitation two squares, the visual square and the tactual square. If they are perceived as a single square, then the judgment is much more complex than the introspective reaction to one or the other. Somehow there must be an integration of the events in areas *w* and *j*.

It is probable that area *p* has an auditory function in the rat, as it has long been supposed to have in man. However, the facts of tonal volume in relation to auditory localization are too uncertain for us to speculate upon the function of area *p* with respect to them.

Localization

The term *localization* can usually be understood to refer to a process that is somewhat more highly integrated than the perception of form. It is true that *form* implies a certain intrinsic kind of localization, since every part of a form is localized in respect of the other parts. However, *localization,* in the more usual use of the word, is extrinsic. It gives the impression of being absolute, for the reason that it places a stimulus definitely with relation to a large and permanent frame of reference, like the objective world of visual perception.

Ordinarily the conscious frame of reference in localization is visual. We have already seen that tactual space is constantly judged as if it were visual. One observes that the tactual pattern on the forearm, created by two stimulus-points, is a 'dumb-bell,' and he sees the dumb-bell in visual imagery. An observer localizes a single point of stimulation on the forearm, and he sees the point even while he tries to find it kinesthetically and tactually with a pointer. He may do almost as well in localizing with open eyes on a photograph or plaster model of his arm, a situation in which kinesthetic and tactual cues cannot occur. The attempt to inhibit visual imagery in tactual localization increases the errors greatly, either because the visual imagery provides accurate cues, or because the difficulty of inhibiting it acts as a distraction. Auditory localization works in the same way. If a familiar object makes a noise, it is visualized. If the stimulus is a tone, given at the two ears in certain relations of intensity and phase, the observer nearly always sees the tone which he localizes—sees it perhaps as pink or blue or gray, as thick or thin, as misty or polished, or what not. The habitual frame of reference for auditory and tactual sensory data is visual.

The frame of reference is usually visual, but it is not necessarily so. The rare observer who lacks visual imagery and the exceptional visual observer who can inhibit visual imagery show that, while vision provides the most frequent medium of localization, it is not essential. Tactual and auditory phenomena can be localized with reference to a somesthetic frame, as they are in the case of the congenitally blind. Moreover, there is the unconscious or obscurely conscious localization, where a motor response follows automatically upon the tactual stimulation without intermediation of any visual process.

Nevertheless, tactual and auditory localization furnish splendid examples of the operation of the context theory of meaning in perception. To the sensory core there accrues a localizing context of visual imagery. The touch or the sound gets itself placed by virtue of its association with a sight that fits into a recognized visual frame of reference. It is for this reason that we say that localization is more highly integrated than the perception of form.

Conscious visual localization, therefore, tends to be intrinsic, a matter of internal relationships within the gross form of the visual field. It transcends itself only occasionally when it requires a motor context. The distinction between *right* and *left* in the visual field is largely a motor habit, which the child acquires with difficulty because there is no clear psychological asymmetry. Presumably the distinction between *up* and *down* is originally no more obvious, though its importance to the organism may lead to the earlier acquisition of the discriminatory motor response.

There is very little that can be said of the physiology of the localizing process, of how the correct visual image or the adequate movement follows upon a tactual, auditory or visual sensory excitation. We are here in the realm of sensory organization across departments of sense—"complications," Herbart called such integrations—and the eventual answer to the problem of learning and of sensory integration will be the solution also of the problem of localization. In other words, localization is either the relativism of form or it is a context; and its physiology is the physiology of accrued contexts or association.

Nevertheless, we are not yet quite ready to dismiss the problem of localization into the limbo of our ignorance. We may not understand fully how a context is added to a sensory core, and we may know that a conscious context is not even a *sine qua non* of localization. On the other hand, it is plain that the sensory core itself must include the essential datum for localization. Psychology has fussed about local signs ever since Lotze invented them in 1852. Everybody realizes that there must be in every localizable sensory excitation some local characteristic that pertains to the place of origin of the sensation and has thus the potentiality for localization. Lotze, Wundt, and a great many other psychologists made the mistake of supposing that these local characteristics must be immediately conscious as 'local signs,' whereas the truth is that the local characteristic is generally immediately unconscious, and is effective only as it gives rise to a conscious or motor context. What is needed, therefore, is a physiological account of these 'local characteristics.'

In the case of cutaneous sensibility we get a hint from the facts of the experiment on the limen of dual impression, facts which we have already discussed in the present chapter in connection with the general theory of projection and Fig. 10 (pp. 67-69). The discrimination of two points can be regarded as the localization of one point with respect to the other. A single point as stimulus gives the perception of a diffuse, ill-defined area. If an observer is asked to localize such an area accurately by pointing, he localizes it somewhere near its middle. Two simultaneous points close together give a larger area; two points far apart give two areas; an intermediate critical separation gives the 'dumb-bell.' It is obvious that there is dispersion of excitation in stimulation with a single point, and that the 'dumb-bell' occurs when the two fields of dispersion are almost, but not quite, separated. It is also plain that this dispersion is related to the lack of sharp contours in tactual perception. What the experiment does not show is the locus of the dispersion. Is it central, perhaps a characteristic of the organization of form in area j? Or is it peripheral, due perhaps merely to the deformation of the skin or to the spread of stimulating tensions within the skin? There is at present no certain answer to these questions, but it seems probable that there must be in the brain some organized pattern of excitation that corresponds with this account.

Further evidence for the existence of such a central pattern comes from the experiments on the return of sensibility with the regeneration of cut or injured cutaneous nerves. We know that the majority of spots on the skin have multiple innervation. The direct evidence lies in the fact that the areas for different nerves overlap, and that severing one of the nerves diminishes sensitivity without establishing anesthesia in such a region of overlap. There is an indirect argument to be made from the fact that returning sensitivity often passes through a stage where sensory excitation (for a fixed degree of stimulation) is abnormally intense and where localization is grossly incorrect. Later these abnormalities are corrected, and Henry Head quite plausibly assumed that changes of this sort would be the result of dual innervation, a later innervation inducing the changes in the earlier.

All these facts of returning sensibility after cutaneous nerve-division are capable of explanation in terms of rather simple principles of organization in the brain, perhaps somewhere in area j. We need, for instance, to suppose that dual innervation sometimes gives less intense excitation than simple innervation, but there is nothing novel in the concept of incomplete inhibition between two simultaneous disparate excitations. One of the fundamental principles of organization in the brain would seem to be selection; hence we should not expect two innervations to make themselves felt at the same moment. It would not be surprising if, in suppressing one innervation, the stronger were weakened, and such a relationship would account for the diminution of sensory intensity as recovery becomes complete. In the same way shifts of localization would occur when the two innervations are differently projected. There is no virtue in pressing these speculations far; nevertheless it is of importance for us to see that a complicated system of facts of this sort is readily consistent with a conception of partially unconstrained spatial organization within a small part of area j in the cortex.

There is no reason to assume that area j should show different regions of projection for different parts of the body. One never becomes conscious of all of his skin at once.

A similar problem occurs in connection with auditory localization. The primary dimension of auditory localization is left-right, the dimension of separation of the two ears. Midway between the extremes is the median plane, a plane in visual space but merely a point in auditory space since localization within the plane may be indeterminate. There are three ways of controlling localization in this left-right dimension.

(1) For a diotic [same in both ears] noise or tone, the intensity may be varied dichotically [differently in the two ears]. The sound is localized toward the ear in which it is more intense. If it is equally intense in the two ears, then it is localized in the median plane, provided the two ears are equally sensitive.

(2) If the intensity of a discrete noise, like a click, is diotic, and the times of stimulation are dichotic, then a single click is heard, if the temporal displacement of the clicks is somewhat less than 0.002 sec. The localization shifts from the side of the earlier click toward the median plane, when the interval is decreased from about 0.0007 sec. to nothing.

(3) If a diotic tone has its phase relations varied dichotically, then the perceived tone is localized toward the side of the leading phase. The phase can be varied electrically for an observer who wears a telephone head-piece, or it can be varied by leading the tone to the two ears through two tubes, and lengthening one tube so as to make the phase lag in the corresponding ear. With the tones in phase, localization is in the median plane if the ears are equally sensitive. If phase is then made to lead for the right ear, the tone sweeps to the right. When the lead has become half a wave-length, a critical point is reached, for a greater lead is more easily interpreted as a lag; e.g., a lead of three fourths of a wave-length is identical with a lag of one fourth, in the same way that a lead or a lag of an entire

wave-length is no lead or lag at all, since the two waves are in phase again. At this critical point the tone disappears from one side and reappears on the other, or else changes so rapidly that it seems to move through the head. Thus the tone will sweep repeatedly about the head as long as the phase-relations at the two ears can be shifted continuously.

It is obvious that these last facts about phase represent a special case of the more general facts about time-relations. The tonal stimulus is a continuous wave-form as a stimulus, but it becomes a series of discrete impulses as excitation in the auditory nerve-fibers. In general, the very short time-intervals that have been found to be determinative of localization for clicks are consistent with the time-intervals involved in the phase-differences of localized tones. Difference of phase as a condition of localization is simply a continuous repetition of differences of time.

Since intensive differences and temporal differences have the same effect in localization, they must in some way reduce to the same effectual cause. Does one reduce to the other? W. A. Bousfield has suggested that differences of intensity might reduce to differences in time if certain rather plausible conditions of stimulation within the inner ear were to be true. On the other hand, it is quite reasonable to suppose that differences in time would reduce to differences in excitatory intensity by the principle that the earlier excitation, making demand upon the same field of projection, would be more effective than a later equal excitation. Of course both views can be held together; intensities can be changed into times at the inner ear and back again into intensities at the cortex.

What happens at the brain? Again we can only speculate. However, the experimental facts make it pretty clear that the excitation which leads to localization is a bifocal projection. The foci for the two ears must be spatially distinct

—a relation quite different from the one that is supposed to hold for two corresponding points on the two retinas. Auditory localization is the result of dichotic stimulation, and we look for the local characteristic after the fibers from the two ears have come together and integration is possible. Perhaps it would be in area p that we find the resultant diffuse bifocal pattern, with its center nearer the more intense focus. The center of such a simply organized form of excitation would be the local characteristic, the essential condition of auditory localization.

Such a view is consistent with our remarks about tactual localization. On the other hand, we must notice that auditory localization is a very special case. In vision and in tactual sensibility we have sensory surfaces which can be projected upon the proper areas. In hearing we have only the two ears, and thus but two focal points, and yet we get at least a unidimensional primary continuum of localization. The fundamental excitatory continuum must be established in the brain; it cannot be peripheral where the auditory tracts are separate. Thus a median localization presumably means some kind of a median excitation between two uni-aural foci.

The conclusion of this section is that accurate localization is dependent upon the relative localization that is inherent in any organized form, that it is sometimes nothing more than the relationships within the form, but that usually it involves some higher integration, as when a tactual impression is localized visually or a visual impression is localized by a precise motor response. The implication is that the cerebral cortex is involved. On the other hand, Lashley's experiments seem to show that gross localization may occur without the cortex. When area w was destroyed and the optic radiations from the internal capsule were left intact, the rats could not discriminate visual patterns, but they could localize visual stimuli roughly in space and even estimate seen distances approximately for the purpose of jumping from one platform to another. Such localizations are of the nature of motor responses, and imply that the projection pattern can sometimes become effective in its spatial relations before it reaches the cortex.

Notes

A general brief discussion of the problem of this book, illustrated by some of the argument of the present chapter, is E. G. Boring's, The physiology of consciousness, *Science*, 75, 1932, 32-39.

Projection and Correspondence

The present author has discussed Johannes Müller's views on the specific energies of nerves and on sensory projection in his *A History of Experimental Psychology*, 1929, 77-88, 92f., 98-105. The same book also discusses the school of form-quality (*Gestaltqualität*), 433-440, 448-450.

To the older generation of psychologists a reference to the topic of nativism and geneticism ("empiricism") in theories of space would be superfluous. To be a psychologist was to know at least something of this controversy. Fortunately the younger generation is freed of this responsibility and therefore needs a reference, such as O. Külpe, *Outlines of Psychology*, [1893], 343-351, 368-373, or V. Henri, *Ueber die Raumwahrnehmungen des Tastsinnes*, 1898, 162-197.

The author's comments about the physiologists' unwitting support of the theory of direct psychophysiological correspondence were suggested in part by the epistemology implicit in the article on the Weber-Fechner law by H. Hoagland, *J. Gen. Psychol.*, 3, 1930, 351-373.

For Bernstein's theory, see J. Bernstein, *Untersuchungen über den Erregungsvorgang im Nerven- und Muskelsystem*, 1871, 170-202. The birth of the theory was the brief article three years earlier: Zur Theorie des Fechner'schen Gesetzes der Empfindung [Reichert u. du Bois-Reymond's] *Arch. f. Anat., Physiol. u. wiss. Med.*, 1868, 388-393. A later exposition is said to be Bernstein's *Lehrbuch der Physiologie*, 1894, 568ff. For secondary sources, see G. T. Fechner, *In Sachen der Psychophysik*, 1877, 138f. (not very helpful); G. E. Müller, *Zur Grundlegung der Psychophysik*, 1878, 374-380 (better); W. Nagel, *Handbuch der Physiologie des Menschen*, 1905, III, 720-723 (good); C. S. Myers, *Text-book of Experimental Psychology*, 1911, I, 221-223 (good, though it does not mention Bernstein); E. G. Boring,

Quart. J. Exper. Physiol., 10, 1916, 86-94 (applies theory to cutaneous sensibility), and L. T. Troland, *Principles of Psychophysiology*, III, 1932, 87-94 (most recent).

The text makes reference to the use of Bernstein's theory in accounting for the abnormalities of sensation when tactual sensibility recovers after a lesion in a peripheral nerve, and to the difference between this view and Head's theory. It also mentions a similar application of Bernstein's theory to the facts of auditory localization. Both these matters are discussed more fully in the text and notes of the last section of this chapter, pp. 110-114, 124-126.

For Köhler's principle of psychophysiological correspondence, see W. Köhler, *Gestalt Psychology*, 1929, 64, and, in general, 58-69, a section which illustrates how much Köhler tends to think in dualistic terms. The other name for this principle applied to extension is *isomorphism*.

The concept of the 'constancy hypothesis' originated with Köhler, *Ueber unbemerkte Empfindungen und Urteilstäuschungen, Zsch. f. Psychol.*, 66, 1913, 51-80, esp. 57ff. In this article we find Köhler enquiring into the fundamental principles under which physiological hypotheses can be established, and he still has similar problems before him in *Gestalt Psychology*, 1929. Köhler opposes the 'constancy hypothesis' only when it is inadequate, when the Gestalt necessarily is a larger totality than the stimulus and its sensation. In *Gestalt Psychology, loc. cit.*, his discussion

has similarities to the discussion of the present text. For instance, he points out that the ability to construct the external world from subjective experience argues for the capacity to construct reliable physiological hypotheses for phenomenal events (pp. 60f.).

On projection in general, see Troland, *op. cit.*, III, 1932, 21-43.

Tonal Volume

The history of the problem of tonal volume is completely given in a few references. For the pre-experimental view, see E. B. Titchener, *Text-book of Psychology*, 1910, 94f. For Rich's first experiment, see G. J. Rich, *J. Exper. Psychol.*, 1, 1916, 13-22; and for his second, see *Amer. J. Psychol.*, 30, 1919, 149-153. The fact that Rich's volumic limens tended to be smaller in the second experiment, where the tones were much fainter, is consistent with the possibility that volume is more closely allied to intensity than to pitch and that 'Weber's law' was responsible. Halverson's limens for volume with varying frequency were merely preliminaries to two other studies: H. M. Halverson, *Amer. J. Psychol.*, 33, 1922, 526-534, esp. p. 527, and *ibid.*, 35, 1924, 360-367, esp. 361. This last reference to Halverson (1924) is the paper on the relation of tonal volume to intensity. The preceding reference (1922) is a study of how tonal volume varies with localization and phase-relation for binaurally perceived tones. That tonal volume should have a definite relationship to tonal localization implies that volume is a true extensity and contributes to space perception as it does in the realms of vision and touch. As to how this organization of tones in extensity might come about, see the author's article, Auditory theory with special reference to intensity, volume, and localization, *Amer. J. Psychol.*, 37, 1926, 157-188. Fernberger's introspections, cited in the text, were never published. F. A. Pattie's attempt at the psychophysical equation of the volumes of heterophonic tones took place in the Harvard Psychological Laboratory; and P. M. Zoll has been working there in 1931-1932. (The proof sheets of this book provide an opportunity to add the statement that Zoll's final conclusion is that the volumic limens, and therefore the concept of volume, are instable. S. S. Stevens is continuing the research.) A number of psychologists (besides Titchener and the present author) have accepted a doctrine of tonal volume: *e.g.*, H. J. Watt, *Psychology of Sound*, 1917, esp. 27-30; M. Bentley, *Field of Psychology*, 1924, 68-70; R. M. Ogden, *Hearing*, 1924, esp. 66-75. For a negative view of tonal volume as a 'primary attribute,' see H. Banister, Auditory theory: a criticism of Professor Boring's hypothesis, *Amer. J. Psychol.*, 38, 1927, 436-440; R. Gundlach, Tonal attributes and frequency theories of hearing, *J. Exper. Psychol.*, 12, 1929, 187-196. R. Gundlach and M. Bentley, The dependence of tonal attributes upon phase, *Amer. J. Psychol.*, 42, 1930, 519-543, failed to verify Halverson's conclusion that tonal vol-

ume varies with phase, and were unable to establish a significant difference between the thresholds for volume and what has been called 'brightness.' Of even greater significance is the fact that the individual differences among their subjects for the pitch limens and the volumic limens were so great that the probable error of the difference between the averages is about as great as the difference. In other words, pitch itself is hardly stable enough in this experiment to be assuredly a 'primary attribute.' One general difficulty with these experiments upon tonal volume is that, when conditions make the judgment difficult, the usual relative judgments give place, without the knowledge of the observer, to what have been called "absolute judgments." In this case the observer's judgments are relative, not to the standard stimulus (which may actually be omitted), but to the chosen set of comparison stimuli, so that the 'threshold' can be varied at will by the experimenter, if he but change the stimuli. Cf. E. G. Wever and K. E. Zener, The method of absolute judgment in psychophysics, *Psychol. Rev.*, 35, 1928, 466-493; L. Gahagan, On the absolute judgment of lifted weights, *J. Exper. Psychol.*, 12, 1929, 490-501; S. W. Fernberger, On absolute and relative judgments in lifted weight experiments, *Amer. J. Psychol.*, 43, 1931, 560-578.

The unpublished experiment on olfactory volume was performed under the guidance of Professor H. P. Weld of Cornell, who is the author's informant.

Visual Third Dimension

For K. Koffka's discussion of the tridimensionality of visual phenomena and the possibility of underlying tridimensional fields of excitation in the brain, see his Some problems of space perception, *Psychologies of 1930*, 1930, 161-187. Fig. 13 is taken from this article, which contains numerous other examples of the same sort.

On the ways in which the third dimension gets itself introduced into optical illusions when the primary stimulus is given to one eye and the secondary to the other (by use of a stereoscope), see E. Lau, Versuche über das stereoskopische Sehen, *Psychol. Forsch.*, 2, 1922, 1-4, and 6, 1924, 121-126, esp. the former on the Zöllner illusion.

On the "glassy sensation," see E. F. Möller, The "glassy sensation," *Amer. J. Psychol.*, 36, 1925, 249-285, and the references to Hering, Schumann, von Frey and Jaensch there cited (pp. 249ff.).

The standard reference for the Gestalt psychologists' picture of the physiology of the brain is W. Köhler's very difficult *Die physischen Gestalten in Ruhe und im stationären Zustand*, 1920; but the conception is illustrated repeatedly in the writings of Köhler and Koffka and others of that school. The earliest notion of this sort within that school was the idea that the *phi*-phenomenon of seen movement depends upon a cortical 'short-circuit.'

The text, in discussing the stereogram of Fig. 12, has avoided unnecessary complication in an argument that is already complicated enough. Nevertheless it should be pointed out here that, even were the doubling in retinal disparity consciously available in perceiving stereoscopic solidity, it would still be insufficient as a basis for the perception. If retinal disparity is regarded as merely the disparity of superposition, then there would be no way of distinguishing between the convex and the concave solids. The crucial datum is the one which is never available to introspection, the datum as to which pattern goes with which eye.

The text also suggests the possibility of a compromise between the areal projection theory of visual space and Koffka's tridimensional theory, and it refers the reader to these notes. It is impossible to say how such a compromise can be made until we have much more knowledge of these things. Nevertheless Fig. 15 has been drawn as indicating the kind of explanation that would be a satisfactory compromise. Let us suppose that ab is the edge of the large square of Fig. 12 as it is imaged on the left retina, and that $a'b'$ is the edge of the large square which is imaged on the right retina. Then cd and $c'd'$ can be the edges of the small squares of the stereogram as imaged on the two respective retinas. The images $acdb$ and $a'c'd'b'$ are disparate, for cd is displaced toward one side of ab and $c'd'$ toward the other side of $a'b'$, just as we can see in Fig. 12. Suppose now that the tendency of similar patterns on the two retinas to fuse is represented by the kind of field of pro-

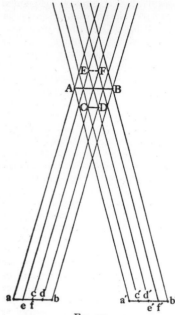

FIG. 15

PROJECTION SYSTEM FOR THE TRANS-
FORMATION OF AN AREAL DISPARITY
INTO TRIDIMENSIONAL DEPTH

In such a system, if there is no disparity between ab and $a'b'$ at the periphery, then there must be disparity between cd and $c'd'$. However, in the field of projection ab and $a'b'$ would fuse into AB, and cd and $c'd'$ would fuse into CD in a plane in front of AB. If the disparity were reversed, as it would be if ef and $e'f'$ were substituted for cd and $c'd'$, then the fusion would be on the other side of AB, i.e., at EF.

---

jection sketched in Fig. 15, where fusion without rivalry means the localization of a pattern at the point where paths from its common points meet. Thus ab and $a'b'$ would fuse along AB, but cd and $c'd'$ would fuse along CD. CD is in a different plane from AB, and the disparity at the periphery is thus translated into actual tridimensionality in the field of projection. Moreover, if the disparity were reversed, if the smaller images were ef instead of cd and $e'f'$ instead of $c'd'$, then the fused projection of ef and $e'f'$ would be at EF, in a plane on the other side of AB from CD. Thus this diagram of Fig. 15 fulfils the logical requirements of the known facts of stereoscopic vision. Is it physiologically possible? Perhaps, although it is much too simple to be probable. Its chief value, in the author's opinion, lies in the fact that it indicates the kind of relations that Koffka's theory is likely to require, and at the same time allows us to keep to the belief in relatively insulated fibers.

Size

On the illusion of the size of the moon at the horizon and at the zenith, see the general accounts of E. Reimann, Die scheinbare Vergrösserung der Sonne und des Mondes am Horizont, *Zsch. f. Psychol.*, 30, 1902, 1-38, 161-195, O. Zoth, in W. Nagel's *Handbuch der Physiologie des Menschen*, III, 1905, 391-393, and F. Angell, *Amer. J. Psychol.*, 35, 1924, 98-102; also the experiments and discussion of E. Schur, Mondtäuschung und Sehgrössenkonstanz, *Psychol. Forsch.*, 7, 1925, 44-80.

To the data of the literature the

author adds his own personal experience (and the experience of some of his friends). When the gigantic moon is seen at the horizon, one can assume the posture for observing the moon at the zenith. Lie down on the back, head toward the moon, with an object under the shoulders, so that the head can be thrown back to see the moon on the horizon. To the author the horizon moon, seen thus, is just as small as the zenith moon, seen normally. Moreover, the visible objects on the horizon also shrink in the prone position of observation. Viewing the horizon moon between straddling legs seems to give a shrinkage which is less striking (to the author) than the shrinkage for the prone position.

Only gradually did the concept of phenomenal or perceptual size emerge. Two centuries ago Berkeley argued that the perception of size is dependent upon the perception of distance, else how can one estimate size when the retinal image varies with the distance? Berkeley was speaking, of course, of objective size, the correct estimation of the magnitude of an object. See G. Berkeley, *An Essay towards a New Theory of Vision*, 1709. Nevertheless, it was apparent that a given object looks smaller at a distance than when near, and it was natural for psychologizing physiologists, like Johannes Müller, to come to the belief that apparent size is proportional to the size of the retinal image. Such a view fitted in with the philosophy that underlies the theory of the specific energy of nerves; the visual perception of size could be understood as the apprehension by the 'sensorium' of the image upon the retina. When psychology came to stand upon its own feet, it did not take it long to discover that phenomenal size neither remains constant like the objective magnitude that it represents nor varies as does the retinal image. Its laws had to be established by experiment, and one of the earliest experiments was that of G. Martius, Ueber die scheinbare Grösse der Gegenstände und ihre Beziehung zur Grösse der Netzhautbilder, *Philos. Stud.*, 5, 1889, 601-617. Then came the alley experiments.

For the alley experiments, see F. Schubotz, Beiträge zur Kenntnis des Sehraumes auf Grund der Erfahrung, *Arch. f. d. ges. Psychol.*, 20, 1911, 101-149; W. Blumenfeld, Untersuchungen über die scheinbare Grösse im Sehraume, *Zsch. f. Psychol.*, 65, 1911, 241-404. These papers give the references to the experiments of Poppelreuter (1910) and Hillebrand (1902) and other relevant experimental literature. In the best technique of the alley experiment (Blumenfeld) the observer works in the dark so that comparison with objects and perspectives is eliminated. He has as a standard the horizontal extent between two distant points of lights. He adjusts two nearer points of light to give an horizontal extent equal to the remote extent. Then the experiment is repeated with the distance of the nearer points changed. From such data there results a characteristic curve along which the lights should be placed to be at all distances from the observer separated by equal distances from each other. If one asks whether these curves are therefore perceived as parallels, and whether parallels would be perceived as curves, Blumenfeld gives the experimental answer. The loci of points perceived as equidistant are not perceived as parallel. The observer can also, under the proper instruction, arrange parallels, which are straight lines. These relationships are not simple.

If one watches another person approaching oneself, it is very difficult to become convinced that the sensory impression of the person gets larger as rapidly as the results of the alley experiment require. (We know that the impression does not grow at the rate that the visual angle grows.) In the author's opinion the failure to find striking changes of size in the approach and recession of familiar objects is primarily due to the inability of the observer to make judgments of absolute size under these conditions. The moving object does not stay the same size; it simply does not seem to change in size because the judgment of size is impracticable. It is also possible, as the text suggests, that in this case the limitation of attention to the moving object may have an effect upon its phenomenal size.

There is, however, another possibility that it would be well for us to keep in mind. It might be that familiar objects do not change size with distance as readily as do the bare extensions of the alley experiment. Objects hold their colors more readily under changing conditions of the stimulus than do unob-jectified visual fields. This is the phenomenon of 'memory-color.' The 'figure' in a visual field is objectified and more stable than the 'ground.' Objects more readily produce stroboscopic seen movement than do simple lines on geometrical figures. May it be that objects are relatively stable in respect of phenomenal size? T. H. Cutler, Visual size and distance, *Amer. J. Psychol.*, 43, 1931, 620-623, sought to test this hypothesis by having observers compare plain cardboard squares at different distances as to size, and then having them make similar comparisons of a light-and-shade drawing of a human hand. The result was against this hypothesis. The square and the hand gave similar results, results consistent with the findings in the alley experiment. Perhaps the hypothesis still remains plausible for actual solid objects (not pen-and-ink drawings), but Cutler's result has decreased the probability of its correctness.

It was also Cutler, *J. Appl. Psychol.*, 14, 1930, 465-469, who showed that half a small page may be as good for advertising as half a large page. It was this experiment with advertising that suggested the one on distance and size.

Form

See also the next section of these notes for Lashley's work.

On form-quality in general and on how the school of *Gestaltqualität* failed to grasp the concept of the immediacy of form, see the author's *A History of Experimental Psychology*, 1929, 433-440, 448-450.

On the history of cerebral localization of function, see the author, *ibid.*, 58-76, and the references there cited, especially J. Soury as the classical secondary source. On the bearing of Johannes Müller's doctrine of the specific energies of nerves upon the question of central localization of sensory function, see *ibid.*, 85f., 93f.

On visual figure, ground and contour and tactual edges, see E. Rubin, *Visuell wahrgenommene Figuren*, 1921.

In general on cortical patterns, see L. T. Troland, *Principles of Psychophysiology*, III, 1932, 94-107.

The question of the primacy of the conscious dimensions arose in the following manner. In the classical doctrine the sensation was primary and its attributes were inseparable and supposedly coördinate. Nevertheless there was a suspicion that quality might be fundamental to the other attributes, for the reason that sensations are named by their qualities, and for the further reason that many statements about sensations cannot be reversed. For example, when we say, "This cold is intense," we do not mean equally that "This intensity is cold." Quality seems to be primary and intensity seems to be *of* the quality. This suspicion and some others like it were voiced by C. Rahn, in *The Relation of Sensation to Other Categories in Contemporary Psychology, Psychol. Monog.*, 16, 1913, no. 67. Rahn was in a way explicating views of Külpe and Stumpf and criticizing Titchener. For the latter's reply see, E. B. Titchener, Sensation and system, *Amer. J.*

Psychol., 26, 1915, 258-267. Rahn had argued that the total sensation is merely a physiological category. Titchener replied that sensation is a systematic concept, and that the actualities of phenomenal experience are the attributes. At that time, this view constituted a relegation of the sensation to the conceptual world of psychological systematization, and thus the separation and freeing of the attributes in independent phenomenal existentiality. It was out of this view that there arose the doctrine of conscious dimensions; see pp. 20-22. This development tended definitely against the notion of quality as psychologically prior to the other dimensions (attributes). Quite probably this original question will never be answered, but will cease to be meaningful as the pattern of psychological interest changes. The text indicates the kind of solution that is meaningful from the point of view of this book. The modal differences of quality between the five senses are primary because they are initiated by distinctly different physiological systems. Extensity, intensity, and protensity pertain to these excitations before there can be any integration of the events that belong to different senses. This argument, of course, does not apply to qualitative differences within a single sense-mode.

Lashley

Lashley's experiments have for the most part employed the rat as subject. The best topographical system for the fixing of localization in the cortex of the rat is a reference to the cyto-architectural fields of Fortuyn (Fig. 16): A. E. B. D. Fortuyn, Cortical cell-laminations of the brains of some rodents, *Arch. Neur. and Psychiat.*, 4, 1914, 221-354. These areas are distinguished by characteristic differences in the arrangement of the cellular layers of the cortex in respect of thickness of the lamina and of the sizes, shapes, and groupings of the cells.

The reaction away from the fixed, persistent, and exact localization of cerebral function began with the researches of S. I. Franz about 1902, and was taken over by Lashley, one of his students, about 1917. It is natural that the work of Franz should seem mostly negative because it showed the inadequacy of the then well-established hypotheses, whereas Lashley's work seems more positive because it, coming later, is able to provide new conceptions to take the place of the old. While there is considerable clarity and definition to the general picture of the functioning brain that is now emerging from the work of Lashley and his students, it is too early to attempt a detailed review of the experiments. They will presumably require both correction as to detail and the further development of concepts. However, the serious student should be warned against resting content with the casual generalizations of the present chapter, but should study the detailed and cautious reports of the experiments themselves. The following references are not complete, but it is easy to find all the others from them.

C. J. Herrick, *Brains of Rats and Men*, 1926, is an elementary exposition of the whole subject of the functioning brain, and draws generously upon Lashley's research up to 1926.

The best general text is K. S. Lashley, *Brain Mechanisms and Intelligence*, 1929, a monograph of the Behavior Research Fund, which summarizes a great deal of this work up to 1929, especially in respect of the learning of the maze. The best short summary and perspective is Lashley's presidential address before the American Psychological Association, Basic neural mechanisms in behavior, *Psychol. Rev.*, 37, 1930, 1-24.

The concepts of *equipotentiality* and of *mass action* are correlative; mass action depends upon the equipotentiality of the parts of the mass, and equipotentiality seems actually in the brain to exist for mass action. On these concepts, see the two references to Lashley just cited, but especially the very lucid exposition in his lecture before the Harvey Society (New York), Mass action in cerebral function, *Science*, 73, 1931, 245-254.

On the visual functions of area *w* and related phenomena, see Lashley, The cerebral areas necessary for pattern vision in the rat, *J. Comp. Neur.*, 53, 1931, 419-478. Lashley's three previous studies on The mechanism of vision are there cited. On the notion of levels of visual organization and of the "fragility" of functions, see *ibid.*, 459-467, esp. 466f.

On the auditory functions of area *p*, see L. E. Wiley, The function of the brain in audition, *J. Comp. Neur.*, 54, 1932, 109-142. On the somesthetic functions of area *j*, see incidental references, as in Lashley, *J. Gen. Psychol.*, 5, 1931, 8. Hunter has made the argument for specificity against Lashley, and Lashley has replied with an account of the way in which specific localization gives way to mass action. See Lashley, Cerebral control versus reflexology, *J. Gen. Psychol.*, 5, 1931, 3-20. But, in this connection, see also the other side of the controversy, W. S. Hunter, A consideration of Lashley's theory of the equipotentiality of cerebral action, *ibid.*, 3, 1930, 455-468; also *ibid.*, 5, 1931, 230-234.

Localization

That localization is normally a Herbartian 'complication' dawns upon one as he reads the detailed accounts of the tactual experiments in *V. Henri, Ueber die Raumwahrnehmungen des Tastsinnes*, 1898. In this book it is repeatedly borne in upon one that the meaning of localization is a relationship between tactual, visual, and kinesthetic impressions. One of Henri's experiments consists in a peculiar way of folding the hands so that the fingers 'get mixed up' and cannot be identified, that is to say, one looks at a particular finger, tries to move it, and finds, as like as not, that another finger moves. Here localization is obviously merely the kinesthetic identification of a visual perception, an imperfectly established organized relationship between two perceptions

in different departments of sense, the visual and the kinesthetic.

For this same reason it is difficult to give meaning to the problem of visual localization within the projection upon the retinal surface. How does *right* differ visually from *left?* What difference would it make if the retinal image were right side up instead of upside down? Obviously such problems can have little meaning in visual terms, since the visual relations remain unaltered if the whole field is reversed or inverted. Localization becomes a meaningful problem in these cases only when we consider how position in the visual field leads to adequate motor responses to the right, to the left, up, or down.

Henry Head's theory is that the skin is supplied with two systems of nerve-fibers. The "protopathic" fibers represent the more primitive system. They usually return first after injury. They mediate all cutaneous pain and the extremes of temperature, generally at unusually great intensities. Localization is poor or incorrect in protopathic sensibility. The "epicritic" fibers usually regenerate later, so that epicritic sensibility is added to protopathic to create normal sensibility. The epicritic system is supposed to inhibit the extreme intensities of the protopathic system, to correct or refine its faulty localization, and to add the sensation of pressure. One of the chief arguments for the existence of two such systems lies in the fact that, when sensibility is returning with a regenerating nerve, the skin first gets hypersensitive and the change of sensitivity then reverses in a return to normality. When a temporal function reaches an extreme and reverses its course, it is usual to look for two opposing factors of which it is the sum. See H. Head, *Studies in Neurology*, 1920, 2 vols., esp. I, 225-329. This is a reprint of the full account of 1908 by Head and W. H. R. Rivers. A preliminary report was printed in 1905, and the experiment itself was made in 1901.

The present author, in performing a similar experiment, came to the conclusion that he had verified all of Head's findings but one; yet he formulated the different interpretation of the facts which is suggested in the text. The important thing seems to be organization in the face of incomplete opposition between independent parts of the system. See E. G. Boring, Cutaneous sensation after nerve-division, *Quart. J. Exper. Physiol.*, 10, 1916, 1-95, but, for the theoretical interpretation and its relation to Bernstein's theory, esp. 86-94. It happens that Head was less sure than the author of the approximate agreement between Head and the author. See Head, *op. cit.*, II, 822-824. On the unresolved factual difference, see Boring, The relation of the limen of dual impression to Head's theory of cutaneous sensibility, *Proc. VII Internat. Cong. Psychol.* (Oxford), 1924, 57-62. The author has argued elsewhere that the two-point limen involves the localization of one of the points with respect to the other. See Boring, The two-point limen and the error of localization, *Amer. J. Psychol.*, 42, 1930, 446-449.

The chief facts about the localization of sounds and the suggestion of the text as to the interrelation of the three factors in effecting localization are given in Boring, Auditory theory with special reference to intensity, volume, and localization, *Amer. J. Psychol.*, 37, 1926, 157-188, esp. 164-173 for the facts.

W. A. Bousfield's suggestion, *Amer. J. Psychol.*, 44, 1932, 805-807, that dichotic differences of intensity would be translated in the inner ear into differences of time is as follows. The more intense tonal stimulus, when frequency is diotic, would have the greater amplitude. The threshold of the receptors must correspond to some approximately fixed amplitude, *i.e.* a certain amount of bending of the hairs of the hair-cells. It is obvious that, when the total amplitude is *greater*, the excursion of the hairs of the receptors must reach the fixed amplitude of the threshold *sooner*. Thus intensity becomes time, although it may also remain intensity in respect of a multiple fiber theory or a frequency theory of intensive excitation.

One expects auditory localization, whether dependent upon differences of time or of intensity, to have always the same proximate cause; in this sense one condition must be translated into the other unless both are changed to a third. On the other hand, it now appears that the relationship between the temporal function and the intensive function is by no means simple. See E. M. von Hornbostel, The time-theory of sound localization: a restatement,

Report of a Discussion on Audition,
Physical Society (London), 1931,
120-127.

The text has regard only to the
primary, linear, left-right dimension
of auditory localization. The conditions of localization in the front-
back and up-down directions and
the conditions of distance have yet
to be worked out, so far as these
localizations are definitely determined. The most interesting discovery in this field is Pratt's. He finds
that, in the absence of other localizing criteria, tones that are high
in pitch (frequency) are localized
high in space. Observers always localize two tones an octave apart
with the tone of greater frequency
spatially above the other. Thus the
use of the terms *high* and *low* for
pitch is explained on a simple psychological basis. That some fundamental physiological principle of
patterning is involved is suggested
by the fact that one observer,
standing on his head, found the
tones of high pitch spatially lower
(with respect to the earth) than
the tones of low pitch. See C. C.
Pratt, The spatial character of high
and low tones, *J. Exper. Psychol.*,
13, 1930, 278-285; but cf. F. L. Dimmick, *Psychol. Bull.*, 29, 1932, 655f.

Chapter 5

TIME

PROTENSITY is the temporal dimension of consciousness. The modern view assumes that protensity is
coördinate with extensity, and that the problems that
arise in respect of the one dimension are apt to be matched
by problems for the other, except for the fact that extensity may actually involve within itself the three dimensions
of space, whereas protensity is truly unidimensional. All this
seems quite natural when considered as a logical matter.
Space and time are linked together in philosophy. Kant
recognized their resemblance when he made them categories
of the understanding. Modern theoretical physics even attempts to get rid of the distinction between them and to
substitute a space-time continuum.

Thus within systematic psychology time has always followed along where space led. Wundt practically began experimental psychology in 1862 with his experiments on the perception of space, and Mach published on the 'time-sense' in
1865 with Vierordt's *Zeitsinn* coming only three years later.
There were nativistic and geneticistic theories of space, so
there came also to be nativistic and geneticistic theories of
time. Wundt's sensory elements had only the attributes of
quality and intensity. When Külpe added extensity he also
added duration, and Titchener followed Külpe. The advo-
cates of form-qualities in the '90's found most of their examples in the field of space, but they always spoke also about
temporal forms. Mach held to the belief in sensations of space

and of time. The best example of a form-quality is the
temporal form of a melody, where the form not only remains
when the quality (pitch) of the notes composing it is changed,
but where the form is remembered or recognized when the
qualities are forgotten. Later Titchener coined the word
protensity to match *extensity,* and Gestalt psychology began
to talk about extensive and temporal Gestalten. Köhler parallels his law of psychophysiological correspondence for extensity by a similar law for the correspondence of "experienced
order in time" with a "concrete order in the underlying
dynamical context."

In spite of all this formal coupling of time with space,
there has never been nearly the degree of interest in the
psychology of time that there has been in the psychology
of space. One may say that space involves three dimensions
and time only one, and that there ought to be three times
as much research on space perception as on time perception
—or perhaps the ratio is more nearly nine, since the complication of relationships might easily vary with the square of
the number of dimensions available for complication. Time
has so little to give to form. Think first of the immense
variety of possible spatial patterns that can occur at a single
instant, and then of the puny paucity of temporal patterns
that can occur at a single spot. Helmholtz's hypothetical
dwellers in a one-dimensional world were almost as limited
in their stock of spatial experience as are we Euclidean
beings in our world of time.

However, the unidimensionality of protensity is not, in
the author's opinion, the chief reason for its relative unim-
portance in psychology when it is compared with extensity,
intensity, and quality. Time is a dimension to which observation itself is generally referred and hence has repeatedly
slipped out from being observed. Temporal atomism is the
most insidious kind of atomism. It is easy to see that a line
is not a row of sensations, but ever so much harder to be-

lieve that a duration is not a series of events, especially if the duration be long. The danger has always been recognized. Introspectionism has called the mental element a "mental process," as if perpetually in the very name to keep insisting that the stuff of introspection is not fixed but flowing on in time. However, there is little use in a name when no one takes its meaning seriously. Because observation in an experiment seems to be fixed at a moment, observed mental "processes" seem to be capable of every kind of spread except in duration. James wrote the vivid chapter on the "stream of thought," with the mental processes changed into 'currents' and 'eddies'; but the introspectionists have always had to be reminded of the figure. The paradox appears in the following question and answer. *Can you observe a duration? If you can, WHEN do you observe it? Not at its beginning or its middle, because it is not yet all there to be observed. Not at its end, because the beginning is no longer there to be observed when the end has come.* Perhaps, therefore, time cannot be observed, in spite of its similarity to space.

Nevertheless, introspection makes it quite clear that short durations can be observed quite as 'immediately' as can extents. The problem as to how an entire time can be condensed into a simple judgment of itself is no more difficult than the problem as to how a spatial form can converge toward a judgment. In both cases the judgment can become as simple as the movement of a finger, and the problem of introspection is the problem of the innervation of a final common path. Let us first see how the perception of time varies in typical cases.

Judgments of Time and Duration

It is plain that consciousness is not so elaborately organized in the dimension of protensity as it is in the dimension

of extensity. We have for consideration in the present section
the judgments of time as referred to a temporal frame of
reference and the judgments of duration as dependent upon
some simple secondary criterion. The 'immediate' perception
of duration—bare 'protension,' as it were—we leave to the
next section.

Long times—an hour, a week, a year—are not directly
perceived, that is to say, there is no unitary temporal organization which can become focused physiologically upon a
judgment. The judgments are involved, intellectual and in-
constant. We tend to judge present time as short when the
conscious content is varied and attention is concentrated, not
because we experience the time as short, but because we have
not been making any judgments of time at all. 'Time hangs
heavy on our hands' when the demands upon attention are
fewer and the question of time frequently intrudes into
consciousness. This general principle applies even to times
of less than a minute. It is 'long' to wait thirty seconds idly
in front of the fire while a three-minute egg finishes boiling,
but how 'quickly' that half-minute goes if one tries to occupy
it with a different activity in another part of the room. The
same rule is obvious in speech-making. The judged time
varies greatly with what there is to be said. A three-minute
speech with ten-minutes' talk to go in it bears little temporal
resemblance to a three-minute speech when there is nothing
to say. The rule reverses for past time. The busy hour that
seemed so short at the time is adjusted in memory to a
duration that will appropriately contain its varied content.

We can gain an impression of how very complicated must
be the various mechanisms of temporal localization during
normal waking life, if we see how such localization occurs
after or during sleep. In an experiment, certain observers
who lived in a quiet rural community were awakened at different times between midnight and five o'clock during long

winter nights; they were asked to estimate the time and to record the conscious basis of the estimate. One might expect under such circumstances that a temporal frame of reference would be almost entirely lacking and that the judgments would be very difficult and uncertain and the errors large. The average error turned out to be about fifty minutes. Since positive and negative errors tended to offset each other, the error of the average was much smaller (about fifteen minutes). However, the protocols showed the nature of the frame of reference under these conditions. The various cues to time were, approximately in order of importance, as follows:

Early in the night	*Late in the night*
Still fatigued	Rested
Inert; very sleepy (except for some observers at very beginning of sleep)	Restless; easily awakened
Ideas continue topic in mind on retiring	Thought vague and scattered; hence tends to center on coming day
No sensations from stomach or bladder	Sensations from stomach or bladder
No dreams recalled	Dreams recalled

Altogether it appears that a person may go to bed at eleven o'clock in the evening, sleep soundly for six hours, awaken in complete darkness and silence, and find within his own body a state of affairs that serves as a pretty good frame of reference for the time.

By contrast with the condition of this experiment, we can see how well oriented in time must be the average person among the sights and sounds of a familiar day-time world. It is not possible always to be sure of what cues we have for time; but let a man, in the course of his ordinary social routine, be mistaken in respect of the time by one full hour, and he soon discovers, first his minor maladjustment to his world, and then the cause of it.

It has sometimes been supposed that the capacity to wake oneself at a desired time in the morning indicates the existence of some fairly accurate unconscious 'mental clock.' Some persons assert that they can wake themselves, after a night of sound sleep, within a few minutes of an appointed time. The facts are not well established, but they would mean little in any case if they apply to times of waking in a familiar active environment where auditory cues are not excluded. Brush has experimented upon himself in this matter, and has found an average error of waking of only about ten minutes. Since these awakenings were nearly all between six and ten A.M., the fact that the errors tended to be smaller than in the other experiment of guessing the time may be due to sensory cues from the environment. At any rate the experiment gives us no ground to suppose that the temporal frame of reference is anything other than the total constellation of visual, auditory, and organic sensory processes, all available to introspection if attention is directed to them.

The judgments of *short times* are less apt to be referred to the general frame of reference, but to be made in terms of some familiar process. A minute can be estimated fairly well by the visual imagery of the revolving second-hand of a watch, but much better by the counting of sixty at some rate habitual for seconds. A comparison of two times of the order of a few seconds may be made in terms of breathing, or of holding the breath, or of muscular strain. It is possible to measure off a duration by instituting with it a process of increasing sensed muscular strain, and then to set up the same process with the second duration, so that the comparison is made in terms of kinesthetic intensity. These judgmental mechanisms for short times need no further comment, except the observation that they tend to be based upon the protensitive integrations with which the next section is concerned.

Protensitive Integration

Very short times are apt to be "immediately given in experience," to be "directly perceived." There is no harm in our using these phrases about perception, although we shall see later that they refer to an integration of the durational events with the judgment. To introspection most immediate data are bare 'protensions.' Almost inevitably, perceived times of a second or less are of this order. Longer times, up to five seconds or even more, may be of this kind; but the longer the time the more likely is it to fall out of the class of 'immediately' perceived protensions and to become the object of a judgment based on some secondary cue or a frame of reference.

The immediate perception of duration is very easy to demonstrate experimentally. A device is arranged to give electrically three successive clicks, defining two successive intervals, one interval from the first to the second click and the other from the second to the third click. The duration of the intervals is variable, and let us say that the first interval is set for three quarters of a second and the second interval is a tenth of a second longer than the first. The observer is to say which interval is longer, and he makes a correct judgment with the greatest ease. However, the point of the experiment is that the observer discovers the nature of a simple protensitive integration. There is no question at all of breathing or of a muscular strain that lays off one interval in intensive terms against the other, or of the translation of time in visualized extension, or of any reference to a temporal frame. To introspection the first interval simply "is there," and the second comes as "too long." The experience is as simple, as direct, as uncomplicated, as is the similar experience of comparing the lengths of two lines, both of which can be seen quickly and distinctly without eye-movement.

One way of understanding this experience is to be found in the conception of a *conscious present*. Logically considered time is continuous, the present is an instant, the past is all that lies behind it and the future all that lies beyond it. If one thinks logically in terms of objective time, the present is a mere point of time without duration, the critical point where the future becomes the past. Regarded in this way the present is specious. Having no duration, it cannot exist as a duration. However, introspection is against this view. The present is quite real to introspection. It is 'immediately given' as a going on, and yet it is all available to the introspector, without having one end lost in the past and the other in the future. Obviously this state of affairs can only mean that we find, in the inescapable fact of an actual conscious present, a protensive integration, a principle of organization that can briefly preserve mental events from instantaneous obliteration in the past, and can pick out of the continuous stream of time unities that, meaning certain durations, *are* conscious presents.

The fact of the conscious present is clearly demonstrated in the phenomena of subjective rhythm. A series of objectively equivalent clicks are grouped subjectively. One hears at least pairs, or some higher integration, like the eight-group, which may be a pair of pairs of pairs. Wundt was inclined to accept rhythmical integration as the measure of the temporal range of consciousness. The classical studies of this problem are Dietze's in Wundt's laboratory at Leipzig (1885) and Bolton's in Stanley Hall's laboratory at Clark (1894). At a very slow rate the successive strokes may not be grouped at all. As the rate increases the number of strokes in a unit increases, or the total group may group groups. The test of an integration is that it is recognized, without counting, as complete with the correct number of strokes, or as incomplete with one stroke too few, or as 'overrun' with one stroke too many. With this criterion Dietze found an integration, at the rate of four strokes per second, for five groups of eight strokes each, which is forty strokes in all and a range of consciousness of about ten seconds. At the rate of one stroke in three seconds, Dietze found an integration of three groups of four, *i.e.*, twelve strokes and thirty-six seconds in all. These are very large integrations and very long times for the conscious present. Bolton reported no group longer than eight strokes, and for this group the average total time was just over one second. With a two-grouping and the strokes given more slowly, the average time for the group was 1.59 seconds. These different results are not necessarily contradictory. It seems pretty clear that Dietze was considering a larger, more complicated and looser integration than was Bolton. Integration is a relative matter; it follows no principle of the all-or-none. Koffka's more recent results accord with Bolton's. In his experiments the duration of the rhythmical group varied from 0.65 to 5.6 seconds, with a mode between 1.1 and 1.6 seconds. The proper generalization seems to be that the conscious present can certainly include a rhythmical grouping that occupies a second or a second and a half, and that with somewhat less 'immediacy' a consciousness may extend to include a rhythm of a quarter or perhaps even half a minute.

There is another experiment that seems to have at least an indirect bearing on the question of the duration of the conscious present. In the investigations of the estimation of short intervals of time, it has been found by half a dozen experimenters that very short intervals tend to be overestimated and that longer intervals tend to be underestimated. The critical time at which overestimation changes to underestimation is called the indifference point and it lies at about 0.75 of a second. For this reason three quarters of a second is recommended as the ideal interval for the preparation of attention between a warning signal and the presentation of a stimulus, for it is the most accurately estimated temporal interval. It is obvious that events separated by an interval of time of this order are easily integrated into a conscious present. The errors in estimation of times greater than the indifference point tend roughly to be proportional to the time estimated, but this functional relation breaks down when the time becomes as long as four or five seconds. It is quite possible that the failure of the functional relation beyond this point is due to the insecurity of integration for longer times, so that on this criterion the safe upper limit of time for the conscious present would be said to be several seconds only, a conclusion consistent with the results of the experiments on rhythm.

In a word, then, protension is as immediately observable as is extension, but the difficulty of placing the 'act' of observation in time has forced us, in the case of protension, to define what we mean by the phrase *immediately observed*. Immediate observation occurs when an integration is directable and directed upon a response which bears such a significant relation to the integration as to be in part a report of it. Duration is 'immediately observed' when a prolonged event is integrated with the response that is the report of it. We find as a matter of fact that this close direct integration does not occur for long times; the upper limit is somewhere between one second and one minute, probably much nearer one second. There is no apparent reason why there should not be longer integrations of an hour or a year, but they do not seem to happen. As durations lengthen beyond the conscious present they begin to break down, to involve loose surrogations of other data for the original protensions, and finally to become mere uncertain relations to a temporal frame of reference. The protension gets intellectualized, and the observation becomes a complex judgment. The integration of the duration with the report is too loose for the observation to be called 'immediate.'

If the reader asks what has become of the problem of the time of observation of a time, the answer is that that problem disappeared when we became clear about the meaning of the term *observation*. If duration is immediately observed, WHEN, we asked, do you observe it? At the beginning with the end in the future? Or at the end with the beginning in the past? The reason that the question baffled us was that it is a foolish question. Observation is a process. It is not instantaneous and therefore cannot be confined to any single moment. In the case under consideration the observation, in a way, begins with the duration in question, and it ends a little after it when the integration has fulfilled itself observationally. However, the truth of any such statement is based on the choice of meanings for the words. It is just as true to say that the observation is the end phase of the integration and therefore comes after it. In either case it is a process, and it can be just as much of a time-consuming process when it is the observation of intensity, extensity, or quality as when it has to do with protensity.

The Physiology of Protensity

Psychophysical parallelism seeks to find in the brain a concomitant for experienced duration, and a theory of psychophysiological correspondence suggests that conscious protension must be paralleled by neural duration. Left in this form the theory gets into trouble, for it implies that mere duration can act as the cause of some event that follows it, without the duration's being represented by some cumulated surrogate, so that the duration is all there at the end of itself in order to act selectively on whatever comes next as the report or observation of the duration. However, we have already seen that this difficulty is avoided when we think of physiological duration, not as a mere lapse of time, but as a temporal integration, the occurrence of a definite process that takes time.

A freely falling body is just such a physical event. A particular fall is a perfectly integrated event. There is no meaning at all in dividing it into a series of events, as if it could be regarded advantageously as falling first through one foot, then through the second foot, and so on, or else as falling successively through a series of seconds. The fall is a single event and it takes time. However, it also does something more than take time. Its characteristics are a continuous function of the time it takes. Thus the total time of fall and the total distance of fall are perfectly represented in the velocity that the body has attained at the end of the fall. There is no false analysis here in saying that time and distance are cumulated in the terminal velocity, because this is exactly what we mean by an integration. An integrated temporal event occurs under some law of temporal organization, and the terminus of a temporal organization implies the whole if the integration is complete. Another way to put it is to say that temporal organizations are evolutions, and that the state of an evolution at any time implies the past. A man is a grown-up baby; there can be no dispute about that.

We shall best get on with our problem if we display for brief consideration a number of cases of physiological processes that use up time. We may begin with what the physiologist calls physiology and end with what the psychologist generally calls physiology.

Fig. 16 shows a graph of a current of action in a sensory nerve. The current is the result of the change of electrical potential as the nerve-impulse, occurring under the conditions of the all-or-none law, moves along the nerve. See also Fig. 6 (p. 40). The process of Fig. 6 follows the function of Fig. 16, and may take as much as two milliseconds in a

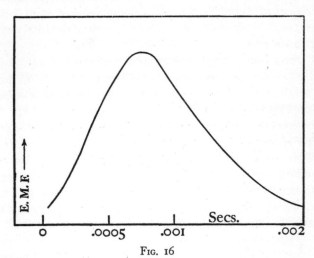

Fig. 16

CURRENT OF ACTION IN FROG'S SCIATIC NERVE

The rise and fall of difference of electrical potential (E.M.F.) as a nerve-impulse travels along a nerve-fiber. Cf. Fig. 6. The current of action represents a unitary physiological event that takes time. After Adrian.

cold frog's nerve. The rest of the process, which consists of the changes during the refractory period, is not given in this picture of a current of action. Certainly the event shown in Fig. 16 is a unitary integrated event, which runs in an instant its evolutionary course. Yet every phase of it, including the refractory phase that comes after it, indicates the nature of the whole and could conceivably act causally for the whole.

Another case where a short interval is of great physiological importance is that of successive summation. Two successive stimuli, each too weak alone to excite an impulse in a nerve, may 'summate' so that the second stimulus sets off the impulse if it comes soon enough after the first. The interval must be very short (of the order of 0.0008 seconds). It has been supposed that the first stimulus leads to some change of the distribution of ions which, when summation occurs, persists until the second stimulus has acted. Successive summation also is found for the excitation of reflexes. The intervals are very much longer than for summation in the nerve itself. For example, a scratch-reflex was elicited by forty-four shocks at the rate of eighteen per second. The facilitation of a reflex *after* the excitation of an opposing muscle-group ("successive induction") may last for several minutes. The occurrence of successive summation in somesthetic excitation has been disputed. It seems certain, however, that electric shocks on the skin, each too faint to arouse pain, will elicit this quality when given in rapid succession. Goldscheider reported the optimal interval to lie between thirty and seventy milliseconds.

It is generally supposed that reflex action is delayed at the synapses. The best-known argument for this characteristic of the synapse is as follows. The reflex time for the knee-jerk has been measured as 0.0055 of a second and the time for the flexion reflex has been measured as 0.0106 of a second. The times of action for the receptors and the effectors and the times for conduction along the nerve-paths can be observed or computed in each case. When these times are subtracted from the total reflex time, there turns out to be a certain increment left over—0.0021 of a second for the knee-jerk and 0.0043 of a second for the flexion reflex. It is supposed that these times represent synaptic delay. The argument is strengthened by the fact that one increment is just twice the other, as would be the case if the flexion reflex involved two synapses and the knee-jerk only one.

It is so obvious that physiological processes take time and that they nevertheless can in their entirety act as causes, that the multiplication of instances is unnecessary. Let us turn rather to instances of sense-physiology, listing ten examples briefly. Temporal processes are the rule where sensation is concerned.

(1) Frequency of vibration is the stimulus to tonal pitch, and frequency is a rate and cannot exist at a single instant. Somehow the time must get condensed into a simple discriminatory response. The resonance theory of hearing is an attempt to account for such condensation by getting different frequencies on to different fibers.

(2) Frequency of impulses in a single fiber is often the stimulus to intensity. An abrupt intense stimulus can give rise to a high frequency of impulses only by setting up an intense continuing process in the receptor.

(3) The fact of adaptation applies to all visual and most somesthetic stimulation. Adrian has treated it as if it were a fundamental characteristic of sensory excitation. In vision there is no such thing as a state of no adaptation; all laws depend on what adaptation precedes their operation.

(4) The phenomena of the positive and negative afterimages of vision and somesthesia are examples of temporal processes of long duration, presumably in the receptors concerned.

(5) The phi-phenomenon of seen movement is a temporal perception. It depends upon Korte's laws, which formulate relations between the time separating discrete stimulations, the space separating them, and the intensity of them. For instance, the greater the intervening space the greater must be the intervening time, if seen movement is to be optimal. The short-circuit theory holds that the second stimulus must

be timed and placed just rightly in order that it may 'drain' the excitation of the first—an excellent, if speculative, example of a nicely integrated temporal process.

(6) The principle of the inertia of attention and of the prior entry of a sensory datum under accommodation seems to hold for hearing and touch, where it is not complicated by the rôle of eye-movements. Stone found that, with expectation directed toward a sound, a tactual stimulus was perceived about 0.05 of a second later than if the excitation were directed toward the touch and away from the sound. Where is the 'vestibule of consciousness' in which the one excitation loiters for fifty milliseconds because 'attention' favors it not? Nobody can say, but if an excitation can wait upon a synapse, it can wait upon attention too.

(7) Judgments of successive stimuli in the psychophysical experiment occur as an integration. There is rarely an image of the first stimulus to compare with the second, but the judgment comes automatically because the second stimulus comes in upon a process initiated by the first stimulus. Köhler has shown the course of this process to be a continuous decrease of intensity after an early maximum—a course that is demonstrated by (and therefore accounts for) the time-errors of psychophysics.

(8) At longer intervals of time we have the operation of the law of obliviscence in the field of memory. While the reason for this law is much debated at the present time, there can be no doubt that the lapse of time tends to make reproduction more difficult or less probable. Especially can there be no question of the working of some such principle in the fading of the memory after-image in the first few seconds after the material to be memorized has been removed.

(9) The classic example of time-relations in psychophysiology is the experiment on reaction time. Under one at-

titude of expectancy a simple auditory reaction may require 0.22 of a second ('sensorial reaction'); under another attitude it may require only 0.12 of a second ('muscular reaction'), thus saving about a tenth of a second. Wundt's original notion was that the first reaction required 'apperception' and that the second did not, and that the tenth of a second was therefore needed for the 'apperception.' This "subtractive procedure" was finally abandoned because it became plain that the difference of attitude made a difference in the nature of the total process, that the 'sensorial' reaction was longer than the 'muscular,' not because it had something added to it, but because it was a longer process. Thus early in the '90's did Külpe recognize the difference between additive complication and unitary integration.

(10) Finally we may refer again to the facts of rhythm discussed in the preceding section. While the process set up in the perception of a rhythm is probably more loosely integrated than any of the others in this list, it is plain that the rhythmical group is much more than a series of sounds, that the earlier sounds prepare for the later while the later fall in upon this preparation, and that each group within the rhythm has a definite evolutionary course that runs itself through in the few seconds of its life.

It would be a very happy and convenient solution to the problem of protensity, if perceived duration could be reduced to an intensity which substitutes for protensity. It is just as easy to make judgments of 'empty' times as of filled times, but the 'empty' interval must be filled with something, not only because consciousness is continuous, but also because there must be some process to 'carry' the temporal judgment. Might there be some such special "t-process," which measures an otherwise empty interval by increasing continuously in intensity while the interval endures? Such a process would be a mental 'hour-glass,' always ready to be started on the demand for temporal estimation. R. C. Moore has some preliminary results that indicate that judgments of duration follow Köhler's law for the time-errors of intensity. [Cf. (7) of the immediately foregoing list of processes.] In the comparison of durations one compares two successive intervals, the second with the first. Moore varied the interval between intervals to determine how the 'trace' of the first time changed with elapsed time. It seemed to follow Köhler's law for intensity. If it were known that Köhler's function applies only to intensity, then we might assume that duration is really translated into intensity, and we could conclude to an intensitive surrogate for protensity. However, we do not know that Köhler's function applies only to intensity.

On the other hand, Moore's finding will be useful, if it is substantiated, because it shows that duration, occurring under these conditions, leaves a trace whose subsequent history can be made out. Moreover, it is clear that, with so few dimensions from which to choose, intensity is not at all an unlikely surrogate for protensity.

All the experiments in which an earlier duration is presently compared with a later duration imply a temporal process, and *a process means that something that is not time varies in time.* In the process of Fig. 16 it is the E.M.F. that varies with time. It is obvious therefore that we cannot rest content with the mere statement of the functional relation of sensed protensity to the 'clock-measured' duration of the stimulus.

We must be careful not to put too much stress on the 'direct' observation of protensity in considering this conscious dimension. It is possible that in experiments for times lying within a conscious present there is a pretty definite surrogation, just as we know introspectively that there may be with the short times outside of a conscious present, where breathing or muscular strain become the measuring process. It is also possible that an observer, predisposed for these temporal judgments finds the two successive stimulus-intervals integrated into a single organization, a long process that sets off the judgment. Either or both of these conditions might be true, with the still further possibility that they apply merely to the artificial conditions of the protensitive observation. Most of the time we are not thinking about time, and most of the temporal processes have no result in knowledge. They may, however, have other results which, being observed, give a knowledge about protensitive organization, which does not presuppose the same processes that would exist in introspection. For instance, a rat makes a protensitive judgment when, in a 'temporal maze,' he has been trained to run twice around the block to the right and then twice around the other block to the left. We must look for some process that distinguishes his second return to the starting point from his first return; yet such a process is not necessarily identical with the ground of introspection in the conventional experiment on the 'time-sense.'

If we seem to come to the end of the chapter with less positive information about protensity than we had at the end of the last chapter about extensity, it is because of the historical fact that much less attention has been given to the supposedly simple psychology of time than to the obviously complex psychology of space. We have disposed of the main difficulty to an understanding of the problem, the difficulty of observing time *at* a time. We see that the physiological account of protensity must be in terms of a process. Since a process is not a mere duration but a change of something in time, we have also disposed of so simple a theory as the psychophysiological correlation between mere brain-time and thought-time. Intensity may be the other dimension of this process, but we have as yet no way of knowing; or the process may sometimes be a process of intensity-in-time, and on other occasions be otherwise. Moreover, there is a certain symmetry between the theory of extensity and the theory of protensity. Extensity reduces to spatial relations in the nervous system, and protensity reduces to temporal relationships. Both relationships are, of course, relationships of something, which can somewhat vaguely be called 'excitations.' Such vagueness is not a fault when it is intentional and considered.

Notes

The lack of interest in protensitive organization and the 'time-sense' is only relative, as the psychologist finds when he undertakes to fill in the gap between K. Vierordt, *Der Zeitsinn nach Versuchen*, 1868, 191 pp., and V. Benussi, *Psychologie der Zeitauffassung*, 1913, 581 pp. An idea of the scope and intent of the literature can be got from H. Nichols, The psychology of time, *Amer. J. Psychol.*, 3, 1891, 453-529; 4, 1891, 60-112; esp. (for ancient history and modern theory) 453-502, (for experiments up to 1890) 503-529; E. B. Titchener, *Experimental Psychology*, II, ii, 1905, 393-404; W. Wundt, *Grundzüge der physiologischen Psychologie*, III, 1911, 1-98; J. Fröbes, *Lehrbuch der experimentellen Psychologie*, I, 1923, 379-395.

Temporal Judgments

For the experiment on guessing the time on being awakened in the night, see L. D. Boring and E. G. Boring, Temporal judgments after sleep, *Studies in Psychology* (Titchener Commemorative Volume), 1917, 255-279. The experiment on predetermined times of awakening is E. N. Brush's, Observations on the temporal judgment during sleep, *Amer. J. Psychol.*, 42, 1930, 408-411.

Protensitive Integration

An experimental introspective study, which demonstrates the immediacy of the judgment of duration, is that of J. N. Curtis, Duration and the temporal judgment, *Amer. J. Psychol.*, 27, 1916, 1-46.

The study of rhythm as exhibiting the temporal range of consciousness is G. Dietze, Untersuchungen über den Umfang des Bewusstseins bei regelmässig auf einander folgenden Schalleindrücken, *Philos. Stud.*, 2, 1885, 362-393. Similar implications (and shorter times for the range) are to be found in T. L. Bolton, Rhythm, *Amer. J.*

Psychol., 6, 1894, 145-238, esp. 213-216. Koffka's times are consistent with Bolton's. See K. Koffka, Experimental-Untersuchungen zur Lehre vom Rhythmus, *Zsch. f. Psychol.*, 52, 1909, 1-109, esp. (for these times) 35f. Another classic is E. Meumann, Untersuchungen zur Psychologie und Aesthetik des Rhythmus, *Philos. Stud.*, 10, 1894, 249-322, 393-430; but this is no place for a bibliography of rhythm. W. Wundt, *Einführung in die Psychologie*, 1911 (Eng. trans., 1912), wrote a little introduction to psychology in which this unity of the rhythmical consciousness is the text. Somebody (Titchener?) once remarked that Wundt started his metronome ticking in the first chapter of this book and just let it tick all the way through.

There is a good summary of the results of experiments on the estimation of short times and thus of the 'indifference point' in W. James, *Principles of Psychology*, 1890, I, 616-618. Vierordt, *op. cit.*, 111-114, discovered the indifference point, but his times were too long (cf. James, *loc. cit.*).

A great deal of the literature on the perception of time is occupied with such topics as the temporal threshold as measured by the rate at which two sensations can succeed each other without fusing, when in the same sense and the same place, or the corresponding phenomena of the 'complication' experiment, when the sensations are in different sense-departments. Cf. Wundt, *Physiologische Psychologie, loc. cit.*; James, *op. cit.*, I, 611-619. Most of these facts are irrelevant to the present problem, except as they illustrate the general fact of physiological latency of process (as in the fusions of color-mixing) and as we see in those facts the simplest kinds of temporal integration.

Protensive Physiology

Many of the facts mentioned in this section of the text are the stock of the textbooks of physiology and psychology and need no support from elaborate citation of literature. For example, on summation in a nerve, see W. M. Bayliss, *Principles of General Physiology*, 1924, 392; on successive summation and successive induction in reflexes, *ibid.*, 489-492; on delay at the synapse, *ibid.*, 426.

On the summation of tactual sensations, see A. Goldscheider, Ueber die Summation von Hautreizen, *Gesammelte Abhandlungen*, I, 1898, 397-432.

For Korte's laws and the *phi*-phenomenon (seen movement), see A. Korte, Kinematoskopische Untersuchungen, *Zsch. f. Psychol.*, 72, 1915, 193-296, esp. 271-296. The working out of the physiological implications of the relationships of Korte's three variables for optimal movement is an excellent exercise in demonstrating the nature of *integration*, as the term is used in this chapter. An integration is no mere summation of parts.

For the results of auditory-tactual complication, see S. Stone, Prior entry in the auditory-tactual complication, *Amer. J. Psychol.*, 37, 1926, 284-287. The classical experiments all used a complication clock, with vision one of the two senses employed, and with the method calling for a judgment on the basis of rhythmically repeated coincidence. K. Dunlap, *Psychol. Rev.*, 17, 1910, 157-191, made it clear that rhythmical eye-movements might account for the results under such conditions.

On Köhler's function for the 'trace' of an intensity, as indicated by the dependence of the time-error on the temporal interval in successive psychophysical comparisons, see W. Köhler, Zur Theorie des Sukzessivvergleichs und der Zeitfehler, *Psychol. Forsch.*, 4, 1923, 115-175, esp. 148-165. Köhler's results are for sound intensities when the interval between successive stimuli varies from one and a half to twelve seconds. If we take the second sound as a standard of comparison, the function is as follows: There can be no time-error at zero time; then the intensity is increasingly overestimated up to an elapsed time of about one and a half seconds; then it is decreasingly overestimated up to an elapsed time of about three seconds, when there is no error; then it is increasingly underestimated with less and less rapid change up to twelve seconds, the limit of the experiment. The function has been verified for other intensities than sound in the Harvard Psychological Laboratory.

Köhler was, in 1923, still thinking of intensity as meaning concentration of ions in the cortex, and his theory at that time followed these lines.

R. C. Moore has worked with the time-errors for judgments of time in the Harvard Psychological Laboratory. If Moore's unpublished preliminary results are finally established, we shall then have to consider their relation to the estimations obtained in the standard researches on the 'time-sense' (Vierordt). Here is the problem. Short durations are overestimated (Vierordt), and durations after a short interval are overestimated (Moore); conversely, long durations are underestimated (Vierordt), and durations after a long interval are underestimated (Moore). The times are of the same order in the two cases, though Köhler's indifference point is about three seconds, whereas Vierordt's indifference point is supposed to be a little less than one second. It is conceivable that the two functions are the same, that a short duration, not only begins to 'expand' after it is completed (Moore), but even begins to 'expand' before it is completed (Vierordt), and that long durations ultimately 'contract' either while they are completing themselves (Vierordt) or in the interval after they have completed themselves (Moore). If this relationship were true, Köhler's function ought not to hold for a successive comparison of two long durations.

On compound and simple reactions, the effect of attitude, and the subtractive procedure, see J. Jastrow, *Time Relations of Mental Phenomena*, 1890, or Wundt, *Physiologische Psychologie*, III, 1911, 424-451.

Hunter has really faced this same question in the problem of double alternation in a temporal maze. Can rats learn to go to the right twice around the same closed path and then start going to the left? It seems that rats just barely can, if they are bright enough. See W. S. Hunter and J. W. Nagge, The white rat and the double alternation temporal maze, *J. Genet. Psychol.*, 39, 1931, 303-319. This article gives the references to earlier work on the problem by Hunter and his associates. Raccoons can solve the problem, and monkeys can solve it easily. Human beings are apt to solve it by acquiring a verbal formula, a "symbolic process." Hunter's general discussion of the problem bears many similarities to the discussion of this chapter. He suggests that there must be (1) "a cumulative piling up in the nervous system of the retained effects of the responses already made" (cf. the total integrated process of the present text) or (2) a "symbolic process" (cf. the surrogative process of the text). See Hunter, The behavior of raccoons in the double alternation temporal maze, *J. Genet. Psychol.*, 35, 1928, 374-388, esp. 374-378, 386f. However, Hunter's symbolic process is apparently not any mere surrogative process, since Hunter seems to think it is an index of intelligence, whereas surrogation may mean nothing more than the "cumulative piling up . . . of the retained effects," if this cumulation is capable of acting causally for the total process cumulated.

Chapter 6

QUALITY

THE concept of quality is usually opposed to the concept of quantity. In general, it seems that differences are regarded as qualitative (1) when they are discrete or (2) when they do not imply a relationship of more-and-less. The differences between the five sense-modalities are, at the present state of psychological knowledge, qualitative because they are discrete. Differences of tonal pitch are qualitative because the scale of pitches has no direction of more or of less; the scale does not imply the existence of a zero at or beyond either end. The series of oranges between red and yellow seems to be as much a matter of quality as the pitches. If we say that orange is complex and that the series consists of varying relative amounts of red and yellow, we have still not avoided the concept of quality since we have now the discreteness of the red and the yellow to consider.

It is a truism of scientific methodology that qualitative distinctions tend, with the development of a science, to reduce to quantitative ones. Inevitably this relationship must follow as long as measurement continues to be the most useful form of scientific observation. The consequences for our thought are that, on the one hand, we must not think of quality as a scientific ultimate, and that, on the other hand, we can no more expect to get along without it than we can expect science to become complete or finished.

It is not true that quality is an important concept only

in psychology. The most striking example of quality in physical science appeared in the discreteness of the chemical elements. For many years the elements were just so many separate substances, unanalyzable, and characterized each by all its properties. When Mendeléyev formulated the periodic law (1869) we had a first step beyond classification toward quantification. Modern physics assigns to the elements atomic numbers from 1 to 92, numbers which represent the number of planetary electrons in the atoms and thus also the charge of the nucleus of the atom. If it were possible now to set up functional laws whereby the various qualitative properties of the elements could be deduced or predicted from the atomic numbers, the days of usefulness for the concept of quality in the consideration of the chemistry of substances would have passed. However, we have not yet attained this level in chemical theory; we have only come far enough to see how it might be attained.

In the same way we must think of quality in psychology, both as an extremely important category because of its usefulness to thought, and also as a category that may some day be reduced, or be logically reducible, to quantitative continua. It is obvious that we need the concept to characterize the gross differences between the senses. Its applicability to differences within a single sense is always less certain, but we still need it either for discrete elementary excitatory processes, or, as in the pitches, for continua that seem not to represent magnitudes.

Modality

Berkeley wrote in 1709: "Sitting in my study I hear a coach drive along the street; I look through the casement and see it; I walk out and enter into it. Thus, common speech would incline one to think that I heard, saw, and touched the same thing, to wit, the coach. It is nevertheless certain the ideas intromitted by each sense are widely different, and distinct from each other; but, having been observed constantly to go together, they are spoken of as one and the same thing."

Titchener wrote in 1915: "You walk into a room, and there see a table; you go into the same room in the dark and hurt yourself, and you complain that you ran against the table; you hear a noise overhead, and wish that the maid would not drag that table about. Here the meaning of a particular table is carried by three modes of perceptive experience."

Thus, with constantly increasing assurance, we have had the idea that difference of sensory modality is the fundamental qualitative difference in psychology, that a sight and a sound and a touch are as different as any things ever could be psychologically, and that the problem of meaning is secondary, so that the fact of the same coach or table being seen, heard, and felt must be explained in terms of relationships between the sensory modalities. However, we face in this section the converse problem as to how the modalities are distinguished.

Suppose Berkeley had heard the coach driving up to the door and his hand had reached down to grasp his portmanteau as he was about to take his departure. Or suppose he had seen the coach coming and had reached for the portmanteau. Or suppose a friend, noiselessly entering the room, had placed his hand on Berkeley's shoulder, and Berkeley, knowing that the coach must have arrived, had reached for his portmanteau. Or he might even have smelled the tea prepared against his departure and have reached for his portmanteau. The sight, the sound, the touch, the smell, all have the same meaning, the general meaning *It's time to go,* the specific meaning *Pick up the portmanteau.* It can be said that the meanings are the same because they have the same behavioral context, the movement to pick up the portmanteau. Nevertheless the case is no whit changed if the context be conscious; perhaps this sight, this sound, this touch or this smell would have brought at once the visual image of Dublin Castle, whither Berkeley was to be driven. Moreover, it is quite clear why these meanings are the same; the various processes all converge upon the same event—a bodily movement, a visual image. Traditional introspective psychology has been so concerned with the variety of sensory cores that the same meaning can have, that it has tended to overlook the identity of context. Modern Gestalt psychology has been so anxious to stress the importance of meanings for the psychologist and to avoid the traditional interest in sensory difference within the same meaning, that it has also overlooked the necessary contextual identity for different modes of the same meaning.

The typical case then is that in which the same object (the coach) by different senses (sight and hearing) leads to the same psychological event (movement or image). The final term intends the stimulus, is the context of it, means it. The correlation between stimulus and ultimate response *is* a meaning, and it is of such meanings—if one takes the larger view of psychology from John Locke to the present day—that the mental life is constituted. From such adequate responses we know how an organism is related to its environment; we also know what the organism knows, for the only test of knowledge lies in contextual response. In respect of these problems it would be possible to get along without stressing the distinction between sight and hearing.

Nevertheless we should certainly not be content with mere correlations. We should seek for insight and continuity, and then we should discover that the stimulus-object produces the same adequate response in different ways, *i.e.*, by different channels of sense. There would be no difficulty about making the discovery. Every one knows of himself that now one channel of sense and now another mediates his knowledge of his environment or his responses to it. The questions before us are: How does he know? In what way is a sight different from a sound?

Of course, the usual answer is: A sight and a sound are different to introspection. The difference is "given" in experience. It cannot be explicated or explained. Every one, it would be said, is aware in immediate intuition of the nature of sights when seeing and of the nature of sounds when hearing and thus of the fact that they are different. However, any attempt to deal with this question in words is sure to yield a false answer, because verbalization is descriptive, and description is analytical, whereas qualitative experience is supposed to be predescriptive and primary. The answer is given, not in words, but by experience itself.

In this manner we are unexpectedly brought face to face with the fundamental epistemological question that underlies the theory of this book. *Is experience real?* In any strict sense the author's answer is, No. Experience, the metaphysical Dator of data, is prior to reality. However, there is a certain ambiguity about the words *experience* and *reality* which suggests the ground of the present difficulty. Objects are real. Now we do not experience objects as such. They are constructs or inferences derived from the data of experience. Nevertheless they seem to be in experience because their inferential nature does not appear immediately in introspection—"unconscious inference," Helmholtz therefore called it. Hence experience seems to contain the reals, which are nevertheless recognized as derived from experience. The layman recognizes this paradox when, convinced that reality is an artificial construct derived from experience, he finds that such derived reality seems unreal. The psychologist recognizes it when, in introspection, he suddenly realizes that what he is describing as experience is, after all, an inferential construct like all other objects and not the great Dator of data.

It is impossible at this point to go more deeply into the epistemological problem. It must suffice that we have been given warning that we are on dangerous ground, and that the path now turns sharply from the usual road that psychologists travel. Is it obvious that a sight and a sound are immediately different as they are given in experience? Very well, the author replies, it is also obvious that obviousness does not always point to the truth. Let us see where this other path leads.

No one will dispute the obviousness of the fact that we can distinguish between a sight and a sound, that we are normally aware of the difference, that we can tell the one from the other. These phrases tell us nothing about experience; they tell us about knowledge of reality. The whole problem becomes simplified as soon as we recognize that we are talking about knowledge. How do we tell a sight from a sound?

We can tell the one from the other because they furnish physiologically distinct grounds for discrimination. Let us return to the figure of Berkeley and the coach. The sight or the sound produces the same movement (or the same image). Starting with the coach as the primary term, we find that the physical light and sound diverge, as it were, to effect stimulation in different sense-organs. Here at the periphery the visual and auditory events are quite distinct. Peripheral localization of function is specific. We neither hear with our eyes nor do we see sound with them. As the projection tracts lead on in the brain, their isolation is diminished by various connections and presumably other means of initiating differential excitation. Ultimately the two paths converge upon a common path, the movement of response; and then there is no longer any localization of sensory function. We have passed, as it were, beyond the perceptual core to the context that is the meaning.

With all this information about the coach and the response to it, we still cannot tell whether Berkeley heard the coach or saw it. How could we find out? Well, we could ask him, and we may feel pretty well assured that the good Bishop of Cloyne could tell us. How would he know? He might know, of course, from secondary cues, as, for instance, from the fact that he was in such a position that he could not have seen, felt, smelled, or tasted the coach, and so must have heard it. However, secondary cues are not essential. Berkeley would have known, and he would have known because some contextual process, the qualitative sign of a modality, had been set up by excitation of the path for that sense, before it became inextricably merged with the path for another sense, as the two converge upon the common path of the common response. He would have known that he was seeing and not hearing (if he was seeing) because the visual path, before its merger with the auditory, would arouse the visual qualitative sign in the way of a contextual process. It is really all very simple. The Bishop knows when he sees because he knows that he is using his visual apparatus, including the projection paths that still belong peculiarly to vision. He knows when he hears by a corresponding process. Knowledge is always a matter of discriminative response.

This theory of modality is frankly relativistic. It asserts that the peculiar quality of vision is our capacity to distinguish vision from the other modalities. A being with only one sense would have no way in which he could become aware of the peculiar quality of that sense, because he would have no other sense-qualities from which to distinguish his one possession. The same rule holds within a single sense; if all sights were bright red we should never known what red is like. So too we are conscious only because the contents of consciousness are forever changing. It has been suggested that sleep is not an unconsciousness, but a state of concentrated hypnotic attention upon a tremendous fatigue sensation. However, a concentrated attention of that sort would be nothing other than unconsciousness. You cannot be aware of something unless there is variety to provide you with a frame of reference for it.

There remains, of course, the question of the locus of qualitative differentiation in the brain. We saw in an earlier chapter (pp. 103-105) that the discrimination of brightness may take place without the cortex, but that perception of visual pattern with any great degree of acuity requires a particular part of the cortex, a portion of area w. It is not necessary, therefore, to suppose that the Bishop used his cerebral cortex to know that he was seeing and not hearing. If he could tell the difference between night and day without a cortex, he ought to be able to tell the difference between a sight and a sound without cortical innervation. On the other hand, we have seen, that in spite of the equipotentiality and the mass action of cortical regions, there is still a good deal of differentiation of function as regards the sense-modalities. (Cf. Fig. 14, p. 102.) We are not forced to assign modal differentiation to a subcortical level, although we may hazard a guess that this distinction is so primitive that we should expect it to survive the destruction of the corresponding projection area in the cortex.

We are now in a position to appreciate the advantages of the present theory over the conventional theory of cortical centers. The traditional view grew out of Johannes Müller's doctrine of the specific energies of nerves. The nerves of the five senses have each their specific energy, said Müller. That was the theory of modality, which Helmholtz thought was as important for psychology as the doctrine of the conservation of energy for physics. However, the only thing that was obviously specific about the nerves was that they were in different places and seemed to go to different parts of the brain. Thus, supported by an increasing amount of evidence (cf. pp. 101-105), the theory of sensory cerebral centers grew up, a theory which is by no means entirely discredited by Lashley's recent research. However, right there the theory stopped. It said nothing more than: If you stimulate this part, you'll see, or that part, you'll hear. It was a mere correlation and ever so unsatisfactory as a theory. Why should you see for this part and hear for that? But if, on the other hand, this part and its systemic connections innervate the process which is the first term in the knowledge that the visual system is in use, then at once localization of function becomes meaningful, and we see why an anatomically or functionally distinct system is the sort of system to provide the ground for the judgment of modality.

Shall we recapitulate? The difference between a sight and a sound is that you know they are different. You know they are different because the visual and auditory systems, before they converge upon common paths, are distinct and capable of exciting distinctive events, which are qualitative signs of the difference. All differences between modalities are thus discriminative contexts or responses to physiological systemic differences.

Quality Within the Modality

Johannes Müller's theory of the five specific nerve-energies might be called a 'place theory' of quality. At any rate that is what it became. The traditional theory of cerebral sensory centers is a place theory of qualities for modal difference. The view of the preceding section is also, in a sense, a place theory, since it appeals to the spatial differentiation of the five sensory systems to explain how the differences become recognized. It was Helmholtz who was effective in extending Müller's theory to take account of the qualitative differences or continua within a single modality. The actual history of this theorizing illumines the modern problem.

Helmholtz began with vision (1852). Here was the great qualitative continuum of color, with its relationships pretty well understood because the laws of color-mixing had been known since Newton. In Newton's day the traditional view had been that the colors were somehow transmitted by the nerves from the object to the sensorium, but this physiology was no longer admissible in the nineteenth century with Müller's doctrine carrying the implication that nervous excitation is a function of the nature of nervous tissue and not of the nature of the stimulus. How could thousands of different colors arise each from the appropriate stimulation of one small point on the retina? The natural way of solving such a problem was by analysis. Newton had shown that all the colors, including white, could be produced by three, provided the amounts of each of the three are variable. If three variables will produce all the colors, then any color can be differentiated from all the others with respect to three variables. Thus Thomas Young had concluded long before (1807) that there are three "principal colors" or "simple sensations," and that it is possible that "each sensitive filament of the nerve may consist of three portions, one for each principal color." Helmholtz seized on this idea, posited three specific energies to account for all the visual qualities, named the resultant theory after Young, and worked out the quantitative relations of the three kinds of excitation.

In general, all theories of color have thus to resort to

analysis. The Young-Helmholtz theory posits three elementary excitations. The Hering theory requires three reversible
processes (six 'specific energies'?), and to them G. E.
Müller added "cortical gray" as an additional central process. We seemed to be forced by facts to an analytical
theory. There is no other way of conceiving how a great
many thousands of different excitations could originate at a
single small spot in the retina, especially if nerve-fibers act
as we know they act. However, the most important point
for us to notice is that all theories of color vision have of
necessity been theories of color discrimination. No theory
has ever done more than to show how a given color sets up
an excitation so specific for it that it is potentially differentiated in excitation from all the other colors. It is a little
puzzling to understand why experimental psychologists have
so generally objected to the functional concepts of awareness,
capacity, and discrimination, when these ideas are pred-
icated in so many of the accepted theories.

Helmholtz came to the problem of a theory of hearing
(1863) after he had explicated his theory of vision (1860).
In the series of tonal pitches we have, of course, a much
simpler continuum than we have with the colors. Nevertheless analysis is again called for and, unfortunately for
simple thinking, no plausible analysis is available. Mach
suggested that all tones are mixtures of different amounts of
dull and *clear* components, the lower the duller, the higher
the clearer. It is just such a theory that we should hold
if we had a law of tonal mixture to support it, if we could
get all the pitches by mixing in different amounts a high
pitch with a low. Since there is no such law, Helmholtz
was obliged to consider every separate pitch as elementary,
and to suppose that there are as many different specific
nerve-energies as there are discriminably different pitches
—about 11,000. This was extending Müller's theory with a

vengeance. The extension was possible, however, because hearing seemingly lacked extensity, and hence the several thousand specific energies could be scattered all over the organ of hearing, instead of all being concentrated at every point as they have to be on the retina. Helmholtz ultimately found the basilar membrane in the organ of Corti tapering in size in such a way that it might consist of a series of resonators, and the famous resonance theory of hearing was thus established. Resonance explained the analysis of complex wave-forms into a combination of tones, and the multitude of specific energies showed why no other laws of mixture were to be found. Thus this theory of specific energies became the usual place theory that the general doctrine always implies. In the theory as Helmholtz left it, the question arises as to why pitch is not extensity, since pitch depends upon place or pattern of excitation in the basilar membrane, but we also know that Helmholtz has not had the last word on the matter of theories of hearing.

It was this place-notion that guided Blix (1883) in his search for specific cutaneous nerve-energies. There had before that time been no simple analysis of complex tactual experience. Blix undertook to use small stimuli to see if he could find differently sensitive spots on the skin which might have different kinds of nerve-fibers leading from them. It was out of this research that there developed the classical theory of four kinds of cutaneous 'spots'—spots of pressure, pain, warmth, and cold. On finding four kinds of spots intermingled in the skin it was reasonable to conclude to four specific energies belonging to four superimposed punctiform areal systems. In such a theory we ought to expect four projection areas in the brain, but the simplicity of the theory has always been spoiled by certain complex interrelationships between the 'modalities.' The earliest of these difficulties was the discovery that the excitations for warmth and cold fuse to give a new quality, heat, which is said introspectively to resemble pressure more than warmth and cold.

In brief, then, the history of the theories of sensory quality is a history of an attempt to get different qualities on to different nerve-fibers. In the skin four 'energies' were distributed in four superimposed and partially interpenetrated systems. In the ear the 'energies' were scaled off along a series of resonators. There was no problem of the auditory perception of projected spatial pattern. In the retina, where spatial form of the projected image must be preserved, there were supposed to be three or even six 'energies,' all concentrated at every point.

We must now undertake to consider the present state of psychophysiological theory of quality within the different departments of sense. We can afford to limit ourselves to three senses—vision, audition, and somesthesia. Any theory of taste would hardly be more than an analogy to the theory of somesthesia, which in turn derives some of its validity from the better established theory of vision. Our ignorance of the psychophysiology of smell is so great, that no discussion of this topic could be quite so dignified as silence.

Visual Quality

In the fruitless controversy that has for many years continued about theories of color vision we come closest to informed, unprejudiced scientific inference in the theoretical discussions of Hecht and Troland. Both of these investigators tend to favor a three-component theory of color vision, a type of theory that fits in with the very exact observations that have been made under the influence of the Young-Helmholtz theory. For the Hering theory it would be possible to conceive of six separate excitations, but Troland—on good grounds, since three processes are already a good many for the crowded retina to accommodate—prefers to think of three excitations for the Hering theory, with the cerebral mechanism tuned to respond to a mid-degree as neutral, and then to differentiate between lesser degrees and greater.

Both Hecht and Troland think of the different processes as localized in different cones. The three-component theory of vision is a theory that posits the existence of three 'statistically' intermingled kinds of cones. An anatomical fact largely determines this view. In the periphery of the retina there may be more than one cone for a single optic fiber, but nowhere in the retina is there more than one fiber for a single cone. Hence there cannot be two kinds of excitation in a single cone, unless different degrees of the same excitation are dichotomized in the cortex. Troland has an ingenious suggestion as to how several different frequency-patterns (analogous to the modulation of wave-forms in radio broadcasting) could be got on to the same fiber, but he himself regards his idea as highly speculative. Hecht finds support for the three-cone theory in the fact that visual acuity is much lower for differences of hue than for differences of brilliance. Obviously a colored pattern would depend upon the stimulation of fewer cones than does a pattern of blacks and whites. For these reasons it seems clear that we should accept, at least tentatively, the notion of several (presumably three) systems of retinal excitation dependent upon different sets of cones.

We have no right to suppose that the excitations of these three systems are qualitatively different in any neurological way. Presumably all nervous impulses are exactly alike except in frequency, rate of transmission, and other such characteristics. A discrimination between two colors means a differential response to one set of relationships in certain corresponding parts of the three systems as against another set of relationships in different corresponding parts. Such a view is still a place theory of quality, and in vision it leads to tremendous complexity because the color systems have to be maintained in the face of adequate perception of extensive patterns. Imagine the visual perception of a library filled with cases of variegated books. There is the areal projection in two dimensions organized as a pattern. There is, if we follow our previous theorizing (pp. 86-94), a reorganization of the pattern into three dimensions. But now we see that either the pattern must be repeated thrice, or more likely every point in it must include three excitations, of which the relationships form a ground for response to color. Or else it may turn out that color perception belongs at a different level from pattern discrimination. In any case the total organization is by no means simple, although this account pictures it as no more complex than it ought to be in view of the amazingly specific and precise adequacy of visual perception. Think what is involved in the perceiving of a set of shelves filled with books!

There have been a good many hints that the phenomena of color vision depend in part on principles of organization in the brain, and not wholly on the working of the retina in the way that the color theories generally suppose. G. E. Müller posited a constant "cortical gray" to explain the fact that there is no visual 'silence,' that there are no gaps in the visual field as there may be temporal gaps in the auditory course of events or spatial gaps in the tactual field. There is a general expectation that the phenomena of color contrast will ultimately be explained in terms of central laws. There can be binocular mixture of colors, which must certainly be central. Troland finds it necessary to posit the existence of cortical "receivers" for each of the three color excitations. Opinions about such matters change as research progresses. We have only recently discovered that the rat needs a certain part of area *w* if he is to perceive pattern, and that the pattern is organized within this region and yet is not literally projected upon it. We shall do well not to try in thought to outfit the visual cortex with too rigid a mechanical equipment. Many psychologists think we are just on the threshold of some new conceptions and perhaps discoveries of principles of organization in the brain that will make the older 'switchboard' theories of historical interest only.

Auditory Quality

The problem of audition contrasts at almost every point with the problem of vision. We were forced to an analytical place theory of color; we posited three (or more) spatially separate systems, each of which maintains the spatial values of pattern, and which together translate other spatial differentials into color. In other words, in vision we require, it seems, a space theory of quality and a space theory of extensity. The two kinds of spaces have got somehow or other to be kept from interfering with each other, and here the analytical aspect of the place theory of color helps us, because it can reduce the spatial differentiation on account of quality to only three sets of spaces. If we had to have, say, 125 separate and individually complete spatial systems, one system for each of the discriminably different spectral hues, we should have reached a degree of complication which would seem too great to be satisfied even in the brain.

In the case of hearing, however, no very great reduction of the qualitative continuum is possible. There are several thousand different pitches and no analytical way of reducing them to a dozen or even a hundred components. Nevertheless, Helmholtz was able to hold to a place theory of hearing for he had no problem of extensity to consider. Moreover, even when we consider the indisputable facts of binaural localization and the considerably more dubious facts of tonal volume, we are not forced from Helmholtz's place theory of pitch. We can argue that, in hearing, the primary spatial differentiation is the physiological ground for the discrimination of pitch, and that extensitive perception depends on a secondary spatial differentiation; whereas in vision the converse relationship obtains, for there the primary spatial differentiation gives us the perceptions of extensity, and color depends upon a simple secondary spatial differentiation. In other words, we have in hearing a multitude of pitches and a meager capacity for space perception; in vision we have an astonishingly acute capacity for space perception and a necessity for only a few (three?) physiological color processes.

However, we must not trust to the analogy with vision to further the theory of hearing. In Helmholtz's thought the place theory of pitch (the theory based on specific energies) was identified with the resonance theory, because in Helmholtz's mind the former suggested the latter, and because the use of resonance seems to be to get different frequencies (pitches) on to different nerve-fibers. It is recognized, however, that a resonance theory of hearing does not necessarily presuppose a place theory. We may have the fact of resonance and a frequency theory of pitch. Such a resonance-frequency theory of pitch was held by Wundt and was recently espoused by Troland. It supposes that resonance occurs and that ordinarily a given frequency is put on to a particular set of nerve-fibers, but it supposes that, if a frequency of 400 impulses per second could be got on to the fiber that leads from the receptor that is tuned to 150 cycles, the pitch corresponding to 400 cycles, not the pitch for 150 cycles, would be heard. A resonance-frequency theory has at once all the advantage that has accrued to the resonance theory from the evidence that the inner ear actually does contain an organ excellently adapted for selective resonance. However, a resonance-frequency theory also enjoys most of the advantages of a frequency theory, especially with respect to the explanation of auditory localization (cf. pp. 112-114). Besides, as we have already seen (pp. 50-54), the experiment of Wever and Bray renders the frequency theory more plausible than it has been at any previous period in its history. A resonance-frequency theory is wholly consistent with these results, because the Wever-Bray volley theory requires that a stimulus of a given frequency should affect a goodly number of receptors, and we can suppose that this situation arises because the resonance is not perfect and a band of receptors responds to the stimulus. After all the chief mechanical objection to the resonance theory has been that the structure of the organ of Corti would not permit the high degree of selectivity required for several thousands of different pitches. Moreover, a resonance-frequency theory is consistent with the results of the experiments on tonal volume (cf. pp. 80-85). The more intense the tone the wider the band of resonators excited, and thus the greater the volumic spread of the tone. It might also be true that low tones would tend to be larger than high tones (when the energy is the same), since the low tone would have a greater amplitude and a wider strip of the basilar membrane would be thrown into vibration.

The chief objection to a frequency theory of pitch has been that it is no theory at all, that it has always left unexplained how response to a frequency could occur in the brain, and how complex waves are analyzed in hearing into their harmonic components (Ohm's law). The resonance-frequency theory provides an excellent ground for Ohm's law. Ordinarily different frequencies would be projected upon different points in the brain and could easily result in discriminative response. When complex and incompleted frequencies get on to the same fibers, as probably would happen with a noise, the analysis into components would be difficult or impossible.

Another objection to the frequency theory is, however, more fundamental. Such a theory requires us to believe in a central response that is differential as to frequency. We must imagine that different frequencies can excite different paths, and thus we seem to be asking for an imaginary set of resonators in the brain when we already have a real set in the ear. Against this complaint it can be pointed out that pitch discrimination is notoriously relativistic; nearly every one can appreciate tonal intervals, whereas a capacity for the absolute identification of pitches is unusual. For the latter perhaps a differentiation of response for a hundred different frequencies is enough, and the important problem of pitch becomes the problem of the perception of intervals, that is to say, of the relation of frequencies. For this kind of discrimination resonators are not suitable. We can make much more sense out of what we know we have, *i.e.*, discrete impulses of frequencies corresponding to the stimulus-frequency.

Let us consider the octave, that tonal interval which seems most probably a 'natural' interval, an interval for which a physiological explanation will have some day to be made out. The octave is the best fusion, the hardest to analyze under Ohm's law. Suppose we have the octave of 256 and 512 cycles sounding. We must suppose now that the octave is analyzed into its two components in the inner ear, and that frequencies of 256 and 512 impulses per second are projected along different tracts of fibers (volley theory) upon different adjacent cortical areas. At a certain phase-relation every impulse of the 256-frequency will coincide in time with every other impulse of the 512-frequency, a relationship that would seem to be unfavorable for the setting up of two distinct simultaneous temporal patterns of excitation. Simultaneous related excitations seem either to combine (as we have supposed they may do in binaural localization) or to effect an inhibition of one by the other. In either case we should have a unitary resultant, and thus the unitariness of the octave would be accounted for. We should not expect as much integration when the frequencies have the ratio 2:3, where every third impulse of one coincides with every second impulse of the other, and thus the musical fifth should exhibit less fusion than the octave. In a similar manner it would come out that the more simple the ratio, the better the fusion—the old rule that we believed before Brues found that the degree of fusion is not greatly altered when we alter the interval by a quarter of a musical whole-tone and thus make the ratio very complex. So Brues's finding offers a difficulty. Another difficulty arises from the fact that change of phase-relation does not alter the degree of fusion. Both these objections could be met, a little elaborately, by assuming certain inductive relationships that tend to bring the two frequencies more nearly in step, at least in so far as they are integrated in a single resultant. However, such speculation ought not to be forced too far, and we may leave the matter thus, with a suggestion as to the physiology of the degree of fusion and with the details incomplete.

In perceiving successive tones as intervals one is, of course, responding to a change in the frequency of impulses. The response is much more precisely determined than it is for absolute judgments of pitch, and seems to partake of the immediacy of the response to the fusions. It is perfectly possible that the fusions are genetically primary, and that the relationships are carried over by 'learning' and 'memory' to the perception of successive intervals. We are not ready yet to discuss the formation of those organizations which persist and recur, and thus constitute the fact of memory.

Let us now repeat briefly what we have been saying about

hearing. Complex wave-forms are analyzed into harmonic components in the inner ear by the system of resonators of the organ of Corti, presumably transverse strips of the basilar membrane. Selectivity is not very precise; a band of the membrane resonates and a group of adjacent receptors responds. The band is larger for more intense tones, because the spread is greater. Low tones tend to have larger amplitudes and broader bands of resonance. The frequency of the stimulus is transmitted as a volley of impulses along the tract of fibers thus stimulated. Projected at the cortex we should find the following relationships. Intense tones and low tones would tend to have large regions of projection. The excitations from the two ears would integrate into a single resultant, of which the locus, according to relations of intensity or time, would determine the localization of the sound. Two simultaneous tones from the same ear would be differently projected because they were separated by resonance in the ear and put on different sets of adjacent fibers. Their discrimination constitutes the fact of Ohm's law. However, they would be discriminated with various degrees of ease according as they were, or were not, drawn into single integrations. The octave, where the ratio of frequencies of impulses is 2:1, would be the best fusion, because every impulse of the lower tone would reënforce and become assimilated to every other impulse of the upper tone. Other fusions would depend upon the ease with which the impulses of one fitted into the pattern of the other. Judgments of pitch are mostly relative and depend upon the capacity for differential response to a change in frequency. The statement that there are 11,000 different auditory sensations means simply that 11,000 such discriminable changes in frequency can result in adequate response. There is no evidence that one can recognize more than 100 different pitches ('absolute pitch'), except in this sense of noting a change in frequency.

Somesthetic Quality

The next sense for our consideration is somesthesia. Here we can afford to limit our inquiry to cutaneous sensibility and for the most part to the relationships of the traditional qualities of pressure, pain, warmth, and cold. There is no evidence of novel psychophysiological problems in somesthesia inside the body. Kinesthesis involves dull pressure and dull pain; parts of the alimentary canal give rise to dull pressure, dull pain, warmth, and cold; muscles and membranes may yield pressure or pain. These qualities differ in extensive pattern from the patterns of their arousal on the skin. It is possible that they also differ in quality, although Nafe thinks that they do not. Organic perceptions like thirst, hunger, appetite, nausea, and sex are obviously patterns of qualities that are familiar under more general names and unique only as regards their meanings or functions for the individual. The skin provides the most useful field of study for somesthesia.

We must raise the question whether cutaneous sensibility includes several modalities or is only one; and first we may note the history of opinion on this matter. Aristotle, in distinguishing five senses, established touch as a single sense, although he observed that touch had a greater variety of sense-qualities than the other senses. The doctrine of the specific energies of nerves was essentially a theory of the differentiation of the traditional five senses, of the modalities and not of the qualities within the modalities. Charles Bell had a clear conception of such specific energies in 1811; Johannes Müller had got the view into a theory by 1826 and into a formal doctrine by 1838. Helmholtz, as we have just seen, extended the doctrine to take account of qualitative differences of color (1860) and tone (1863), seemingly without realizing at the time that the doctrine had been doing service as a theory of modality and that he was now extending it to intramodal quality. It seems not to have been until 1878 that Helmholtz used the word *Modalität* for the different senses, and defined a modality as a qualitative system discontinuous with other coördinate qualitative systems.

Meanwhile the complexity of cutaneous sensibility had been continuously recognized, although there had been no permanent subdivision of the sense. E. H. Weber (1846) distinguished the *Gemeingefühl* (which included pain) from the *Tastsinn,* which was in turn divided into a *Drucksinn,* a *Temperatursinn* and an *Ortsinn.* Obviously Weber was using the word *Sinn* loosely as sensibility and not as a sense-department. No clear view emerged until Blix in 1883, seeking to study specific nerve-energies for the skin and working with small stimuli, discovered pressure, warmth, and cold spots, and concluded of course that he had discovered three kinds of nerves. Goldscheider verified the gross fact of Blix's discovery the next year. Pain spots were somewhat uncertainly added to the list. It was von Frey who dressed this theory up in good clothes and successfully presented it to psychology. He made it clear that pressure, warmth, cold, and pain are four distinct modalities, and he attached to each of the four, by a not incontrovertible argument (as it proved), a separate sense-organ. However, it was only in 1920 that Titchener was trying to bring all the cutaneous qualities into one continuum by means of his "touch pyramid," and in 1927 that Nafe was reporting an experiment that told against all these qualitative distinctions in touch. Von Frey's correlations with sense-organs were never established, except for the relation of pressure spots to hair follicles. Goldscheider (1886) and Dallenbach (1927) found at cold and warm spots nothing but free nerve-endings, the endings that were supposed by von Frey to function for pain.

All this history is important because it has been incorrectly stated that the doctrine of four cutaneous modalities, unsupported in fact, is an erroneous view fixed upon psychology for a century by the great prestige of Johannes Müller. The four modalities date from the relatively unimportant Blix, in 1883; there were important objectors at once, like Dessoir (1892); von Frey made it the standard view about 1895; but, except for the elementary textbooks where the expert voice is but faintly heard, there was a good deal of doubt all along. For not a great deal more than twenty-five years (1895-1920) has von Frey's theory been the belief of many experts.

Let us now get our facts in order. Temperature spots are easily demonstrated on the skin. A metal point much colder than the skin, when dragged across the skin, brings out the bright cold sensation at tiny areas and elicits no cold in between. There may be a dozen such spots in a square centimeter on the back of the hand. If the point is a few degrees above the temperature of the skin, then diffuse sensations of warmth are found, the spots are large and there may be only two or three in the same square centimeter that contained the dozen cold spots. The two kinds of spots appear to be distributed without relation to each other; a spot on the skin may be sensitive to both warmth and cold, to either, or to neither. A very warm stimulus on a cold spot may give rise to 'paradoxical' cold. Hence a very warm stimulus on both warm and cold spots ought to give rise to a cold warmth, but actually this fusion is reported as a new quality, 'heat,' which is said to resemble pressure and pain introspectively. Heat can be experimentally aroused by cold on a cold spot with warmth on an adjacent warm spot.

Adaptation to warmth means sensitization to cold, and *vice versa*. The evidence from the spots favors separate receptors. The evidence from adaptation and from fusion in heat favors a single mechanism.

However, the evidence from the spots is not univocal. The spots are the places that are relatively sensitive to warmth and cold respectively. In between them are large doubtful areas. Sometimes it seems as if there were almost no part of the skin from which a vague fleeting warmth or cold could not be aroused by the appropriate stimulus if the thermal difference from the skin is fairly great. Some spots can be marked and their location verified day after day, but in general it is very difficult to duplicate in a second exploration the thermal topography of a first one. The spots seem to vary in sensitivity. Von Frey recognized the fact that, in order to get consistent topographical results, the observer must learn the *Merkmale* of warmth or cold, which may easily mean that he is to take the 'honest-to-goodness' spots and leave the 'doubtfuls' alone. Probably Goldscheider counted the 'doubtfuls,' since he found very many more spots than von Frey. Excision of the positive spots and histological examination of the excised tissue reveals no nervous structure but free endings, which are distributed ever so much more densely than is required by the conventional topography of the temperature spots. Histologically all the cutaneous receptors look alike.

In brief, then, we are sure only of an uneven distribution of sensitivity to warmth and a differently uneven distribution of sensitivity to cold. It is possible that all or nearly all of the skin is sensible to warmth and to cold if the stimulus be effective enough. The resultant vague warmths are often confused with pressure; the faint colds may resemble prick. In any case warmth and cold are related in that they involve antagonistic processes. If they have separate receptors, at least the receptors must be involved in a common mechanism.

The existence of pressure spots seems to be established by the observed relation of the spots to the hairs of the skin, every pressure spot 'to the windward' of a hair, as if the free endings of nerve-fibers at the hair-follicles were the receptors. There is no doubt about this topographical correlation if one considers only the 'honest-to-goodness' pressures, the 'solid,' 'granular' pressure sensations, which have the traditional *Merkmale*. It is presumably this sort of pressure that occurs when the hairs are touched; they act as sensitive levers to excite the nerve-terminations near their bases. However, all pressure sensations of the skin do not come from these spots. A light touch upon the intervening regions, such as can be made with the end of a piece of horse-hair as a stimulus, practically always gives rise to some sort of vague, light, pressure sensation, an experience that is the sensory core of 'tickle' and one that has been given the technical name 'contact.' It is not at all certain that this contact and the granular pressure are qualitatively different, and thus with pressure, as with temperature, the 'spot' theory turns out to be only a gross approximation. The skin can everywhere be stimulated by light pressure to give the sensory response called 'pressure'; the hairs are especially effective organs and thus the spots over the hair-follicles are very sensitive spots; and elsewhere one finds variability without complete insensitivity at any point.

The pain spots never really did get established. Von Frey believed in them, but they are so densely distributed—a couple to the square millimeter—as to be incapable of accurate mapping. The prick quality comes out for a thrust of a needle at any point in the skin. Again there is variability in sensitivity, and the needle must penetrate deeper in some places than in others. Hence, with little weight upon the needle, the investigator finds pain spots with analgesic spaces in between, but the analgesia seems to be simply an artifact of a weak stimulus. It is probably true that the conical point of a needle cannot penetrate far into the skin without affecting at least some one of the very numerous free nerve-endings.

All along there had been doubt as to whether pain might not be "common sensibility" or a "summation sense." The ground for this view lay in the fact that all very intense stimuli—blinding lights, deafening sounds, extreme heat and extreme cold—tend to arouse pain. May not the pain of the brilliant light come from the optic fibers themselves? Is it not possible that the direct stimulation of any nerve-fiber gives rise to pain, a sensation common to all nerves? Or at least may it not be true that extreme pressure, warmth, or cold results in pain by way of summation? These definite theories have mostly been dismissed. Visual and auditory pain comes from the extremes of muscular accommodation to a very intense stimulation, and is truly somesthetic. There is certainly no convincing evidence for a summation sense. The simplest theory is that there are pain receptors which become involved in any kind of intense somesthetic stimulation, or that pain *is* merely intense somesthesia. This latter view is Nafe's.

Our knowledge of cutaneous sensibility, as it bears on the problem of modality, boils down to the following statements. There are receptors for cutaneous somesthesia, the free endings in the skin. In this sense there are certainly sensory 'spots.' No histological difference among these free endings has been clearly established (although it is possible that there are two or three kinds of free endings). It is certainly true that the histology of these cutaneous receptors furnishes no more ground for a belief in different kinds of receptors than does the histology of the retinal cones or of the cochlear hair-cells in the cases of vision and hearing.

On the other hand, it is equally true that histology does not tell against a theory of the differentiation of cutaneous receptors for it seems unlikely that a functional difference should be microscopically visible. Thus we come back to Blix's original discovery as our principal positive fact, viz., that there is a difference in the topography of the sensitivity to cold, to warmth, and to pressure.

Nafe has recently argued against a plurality of somesthetic modalities with what he calls a "quantitative theory of feeling." He has exhibited in a careful, experimental, introspective study, the qualitative similarities and confusions amongst the supposedly modal differences. Faint warmth is confused with pressure. Cold and prick are alike. Heat, a fusion of cold and warmth stimulations, is a prickly pressure. "Brightness" seems to be *the* cutaneous quality and intensitive-extensitive-protensitive patterns of it may account for the variation that occurs. Nafe also appeals to the facts of stimulation. Cold and warmth fuse in heat and are otherwise opposed in stimulation as well as in adaptation. Pain is associated with any intense stimulation and might thus be the pattern for intense stimulation. There is no anatomical evidence for differentiation, for the free nerve-endings all look alike. There is no physiological evidence for differentiation, and stimuli that would be expected to excite pain in an animal are found to give rise to higher frequencies of impulses in the nerve than stimuli that would be expected to excite only pressure. (This last point is merely negative, because it is not inconsistent with a theory of plural modalities that pain should always be associated with the violent excitation that involves other modalities.)

Nafe has next asked about the capacities of cutaneous nerves for differentiated conduction of afferent excitation. He suggests four presumptive dimensions of variation and four corresponding "conscious experiences"; thus:

Physiological Dimension	*Conscious Dimension*
1. Frequency of the impulses	1. Intensity
2. Duration of excitation	2. Protensity
3. Area of excitation	3. Extensity
4. Number of fibers excited within the area	4. Density

Nafe's fourth dimension, *density*, does not of course serve as a direct substitute for the abandoned dimension, *quality*. He does not need a fourth dimension for his view, since he argues that what has been supposed to be quality is really the pattern of (relationship among) the first three dimensions. However, Nafe is clearly wrong in thinking that all the properties of a nerve lie in the nerve itself. The Helmholtzian place theory of quality is an explanation of how two fibers, exactly alike, carrying impulses, exactly alike, are nevertheless differentiated by the loci of their central terminations.

Nafe's view is not impossible, although it seems like a flouting of introspective facts. You experience, let us say, a warmth of a given intensity, extensity, and protensity. How do you change it into a cold of a given (perhaps similar?) intensity, extensity, and protensity? We are scarcely to be expected to believe that we make the change by altering intensity, extensity, and protensity—unless we are given some definite account of the way the change is made. So the change must be primarily in density, and here we can see that perhaps all colds are dense and all warmths diffuse. What then should we do about pressure? Well, pressure might be an intermediate density, or it might be a weak warmth-or-cold, a fact which would explain why heat, a mixture of antagonistic warmth and cold, is 'pressury.' And pain is intense warmth-cold. This is a possible view, although it seems to the present author improbable.

It seems improbable because it is not necessary, and it is

hardly likely that all sensory qualities—colors, pitches, touches—are to be got rid of so simply by identifying them with intensitive-extensitive-densitive patterns. After all the skin resembles the retina, and whatever theory works for the retina offers a possibility for the skin. The skin presents less complex problems than the retina, and two free endings in it do not look any more alike than two cones in the retina.

At any rate a conventional and plausible theory of somesthetic quality could run as follows. There are four kinds of receptors in the skin—for warmth, cold, pressure, and pain. Respectively, their adequate stimuli are (1) temperature above the level of cutaneous adaptation, (2) temperature below the level of adaptation, (3) mechanical pressure, and (4) a large change of energy at the receptor. Obviously the stimulus implied by (4) is any strong stimulus of the nature of (1), (2) or (3), or a stimulus, like a needle, that penetrates directly to the receptor. Most adequate stimuli of one class are inadequate stimuli of the other classes. We are much less likely to experience one of these qualities pure than we are to see a pure color, like a blue that is neither reddish nor greenish. Fusion is the rule of the skin and of the retina, and confusion results more for the skin because discrimination in all dimensions is less precise.

There must be some mechanism of opposition between warmth and cold. Nafe suggests that it might be peripheral and muscular, like a tension for cold and a relaxation for warmth. Such a view is consistent with the notion of two receptors, one for tension and one for relaxation. If the opposition is neural and peripheral, we might have to conceive of a single thermal receptor, the seat of a process which deviates above and below a point of equilibrium—a view like Troland's for a cone that would work according to the

Hering theory of vision (pp. 162f.). However, the opposition might be central. Color-mixture requires a central explanation in the form of a response to differential excitations between three or more systems. The facts of heat seem to require a similar explanation.

It is not unreasonable to regard pain as an intense degree of anything else in somesthesia. The sole difficulty lies in the answer to the question as to how pain, if it is intensity, ever got itself differentiated from intensity. There cannot be two different responses to the same condition. If all intense cutaneous stimulations were painful, we never should have been able to discriminate between them. The old summation theory assumed that an intense pressure involves such violent excitation that, besides exciting the normal projection areas intensely, it also jumps over to a 'pain' tract and excites that projection area, too. A simple psychophysical parallelism would say then: Two regions, two experiences. However, we have set ourselves the much more difficult task of enquiring into the physiology of introspection, and even so simple a physiology as is implied by the concept of the conditioned reflex makes it seem improbable that pain could be discriminated from pressure, if it were always a concomitant of intense pressure. On the other hand, if we accept the distinction between pressure and temperature, or between pressure, warmth, and cold, and regard pain as an invariable concomitant of extremes in these modalities, then there is no reason to believe that it should not have become abstracted from the qualities with which it is associated, for no one of the other qualities is the invariable concomitant of pain. On these grounds, we could accept a summation theory of pain, if there should be other grounds to support it.

In brief, then, what we want is to keep the four fundamental qualities of somesthesia—pressure, pain, warmth, and cold. They are constantly being fused and confused. They have certain definite interrelations which require that they be considered as forming a single modality. At most there may be four kinds of receptors, one for each of these fundamental qualities. At least there should be two kinds of receptors, since pain may be a "summation sensation," since there may be but a single receptor for warmth and cold, and since there are needed at least two other modalities to explain the differentiation of pain if it occurs as summation without a specific receptor. Any further elaboration of a theory of somesthetic perception would follow the lines already laid out for visual perception, and would also meet with most of the difficulties that appear in visual theory.

Notes

There is no advantage to be derived from pressing the distinction between qualitative and quantitative to the limits of an irreproachable logic. The distinction arises because qualitative differences are generally supposed to be unmeasurable or at least inexactly describable. There is also the general belief that 'qualification' gives place historically in science to quantification. The useful cue to the difference, however, lies in the concept of discreteness, but we are also forced to go further and to equate 'quantity' to magnitude, i.e., to refer it to a zero-point. All this problem is tied up with the tendency of the scientific mind to reify its concepts (qualitative distinction) and then to deal with amounts of the resultant entities (quantitative distinction). But the uniformity of nature (the economy of thought?) requires the reduction of the many entities to a few as knowledge advances. On the other hand, we can urge that atomic numbers are discrete; but then so are the quanta of light as well as the sensory j.n.d.'s of intensity. We must not press the logic too vigorously.

Titchener has discussed this general matter, distinguishing between the qualitative attributes, on the one hand, and the "intensive" attributes of intensity proper, extensity, and protensity, on the other. See E. B. Titchener, *Lectures on the Elementary Psychology of Feeling and Attention*, 1908, 3-30, 321-327. Titchener was here influenced by Müller, who had brought up the matter of the zero-point. See G. E. Müller, Zur Psychophysik der Gesichtsempfindungen, *Zsch. f. Psychol.*, 10, 1896, 1-4, 25-33. But of course Müller and Titchener had no suppressed desire to see conscious quality reduced to something else.

On the general psychophysiology of quality, see L. T. Troland, *Principles of Psychophysiology*, III, 1932, 109-128.

Modality

On the differentiation of meaning from sensory quality (and for the quotations that introduce the section), see G. Berkeley, *An Essay Towards a New Theory of Vision*, 1709, pars. 9, 10, 16-18, 45-47; E. B. Titchener, *A Beginner's Psychology*, 1915, 26-30.

For references to the context theory of meaning, see the author's *A History of Experimental Psychology*, 1929, 429. Of course the theory of meaning of the present book is much more general than Titchener's. Here a *context* is regarded as a response, and a *response* is necessarily some kind of a *context*. A context of imagery is a response; a discriminative response to a stimulus is a context that gives meaning to the stimulus as stimulus.

The discussion of the text suggests why the comparison of attributes across modalities is difficult. It is possible to equate the pressure of a weight to the loudness of a tone, but not with great reliability. One can do better in comparing tactual and visual extents, but then the reference is apt to be to some visualized common denominator, like a centimeter scale. Brightnesses of tones, odors, and colors can be equated without great consistency of results. Obviously in such equations it is necessary to establish a differential between unintegrated excitations. This is a very much more complex and less certain matter than the establishment of a differential relation between two immediately successive intensities of a noise, where the difference lies as a change in an intensity within an integration.

Intramodal Quality

For a discussion of Johannes Müller's doctrine of specific energies, Helmholtz's extension of the doctrine to qualitative difference within the modality, Helmholtz's use of the extended doctrine in his theories of vision and of hearing, what Thomas Young actually said about color theory, what Blix and the others did to find cutaneous specific energies, and the references to all these original sources, see the author's *A History of Experimental Psychology*, 1929, 77-94; also 283-295, 298f., 308.

For Mach's theory of the dull and clear elements in pitch, see E. Mach, *The Analysis of Sensations*, Eng. trans., 5th German ed., 1914, 291-299, or the corresponding discussion in the earlier editions in the chapter, The sensations of tone.

On the fusion of excitations for warmth and cold to give heat, see S. Alrutz's easily accessible account in English, *Mind*, N. S. 7, 1898, 141-144; F. Cutolo, *Amer. J. Psychol.*, 29, 1918, 442-448; J. H. Alston, *ibid.*, 31, 1920, 303-312; N. C. Burnett and K. M. Dallenbach, *ibid.*, 38, 1927, 418-431.

Visual Quality

On the psychophysiology of visual perception, see especially L. T.

Troland, *Principles of Psychophysiology*, II, *Sensation*, 1930, a great deal of 51-205, but esp. 121-136, which is mostly on Hecht's theories, and 187-202, which is Troland's own theorizing. Then see S. Hecht, *The Retinal Processes Concerned with Visual Acuity and Color Vision* (Howe Lab. Ophthalmol., Harvard Med. Sch., Bull. no. 4), 1931, esp. chaps. 1, 3, 5, 11. See also Hecht, in *Foundations of Experimental Psychology*, 1929, 216-272.

Troland is discussing a possible neurological basis for the Ladd-Franklin theory of color vision when he suggests modulation of frequency-patterns in a single nerve-fiber, *op. cit.*, 200f.

As an example of the need for special cortical processes in explaining the facts of color vision, or at least for processes at more than one neurological level, see C. E. Ferree and G. Rand, Some areas of color blindness of an unusual type in the peripheral retina, *J. Exper. Psychol.*, 2, 1917, 295-303, and the similar views of Schumann and G. E. Müller there cited.

In view of the plausibility of a frequency theory of pitch, the question arises as to why a frequency theory of color is not equally inviting. However, the frequency of light is several hundred thousand billion vibrations per second, a rate far removed from the capacities of nervous tissue. Yet the frequencies are differentially effective and thus one looks to photochemical reactions which can be selective in this way (as they are on the photographic plate). The evidence for this sort of reaction in the retina is

now conclusive; cf. Hecht, in *Foundations, loc. cit.*

Auditory Quality

For a competent resonance-frequency theory of hearing, see Troland, *op. cit.*, 254-260. The idea that a frequency theory does not preclude the belief in resonance in the inner ear is not new. Wundt and Ebbinghaus both had resonance-frequency theories. See W. Wundt, *Grundzüge der physiologischen Psychologie*, II, 1910, 131-136; H. Ebbinghaus, *Grundzüge der Psychologie*, I, 1905, 330-346. Troland's entire discussion, 240-260, is much in point. In places its inferences differ markedly from the interpretations of the present text.

A modern experimental study of the degrees of tonal fusion is that of C. C. Pratt, Some qualitative aspects of bitonal complexes, *Amer. J. Psychol.*, 32, 1921, 490-515. For Brues on fusions of quarter-tone tempered intervals, see A. M. Brues, The fusion of non-musical intervals, *ibid.*, 38, 1927, 624-638, a paper which includes an excellent summary of various classical theories, 626f. It must be observed that any theory of tonal fusion that is based upon the simplicity of ratios of the stimulus-frequencies must also include some principle of assimilation, whereby a ratio that is close to a simple ratio functions as if it were the approximate simple ratio. On any other case slight mistunings would ruin fusion utterly. The ratio 2:3 is the simple ratio for the musical fifth, but a variation of one tenth of one per cent in the difference between the two frequencies would change the ratio to 2000:2999, without a possibility of substituting simpler numbers. Thus the ratio for the fifth in the musical tempered scale is theoretically a ratio of incommensurables, $1:^{12}\sqrt{2^7}$. Plainly these theoretical values are only approximated in practice.

The reader may be again referred to the author's advocacy of a frequency theory in relation to the problems of auditory volume and localization, *Amer. J. Psychol.*, 37, 1926, 157-188.

Somesthetic Quality

On the reduction of the various visceral and organic perceptions to the fundamental qualities of pressure, pain, warmth, and cold, see the text and notes of chapter 2, pp. 25f., 33f.

A secondary reference to the history of the theory of specific energies of nerves has been given above. For Helmholtz on modality (a lecture in 1878), see H. v. Helmholtz, *Die Thatsachen in der Wahrnehmung*, 1879, 8-13 (reprinted in *Vorträge und Reden*, 1884, II, 223-226).

For Weber's subdivision of the sense of touch, see E. H. Weber, *Der Tastsinn und das Gemeingefühl*, in R. Wagner's *Handwörterbuch der Physiologie*, III, ii, 1846, 481-588; and later separates.

The first application of the theory of specific energies to touch was made by M. Blix, Experimentelle Beiträge zur Lösung der Frage über die specifische Energie der Haut-

nerven, *Zsch. f. Biol.*, 20, 1884, 141-156; 21, 1885, 145-160 (the original publication is cited as in the much less available *Upsala läkareförenings förhandlingar*, 18, 1883, 87ff.). For Goldscheider's extensive researches in cutaneous psychophysiology, see A. Goldscheider, *Gesammelte Abhandlungen*, 1898, I, esp. 53-218 which is the reprinting of six papers appearing in 1884-1885. One of the early skeptics was M. Dessoir, Ueber den Hautsinn, *Arch. f. Physiol.*, 1892, 175-339 (also separate). For the 'traditional' theory of cutaneous sensation, see M. von Frey, the four short papers in *Ber. d. kgl. sächs. Gesellsch. d. Wiss. zu Leipzig, math.-phys. Cl.*, 46, 1894, 185-196, 283-296; 47, 1895, 166-184 (end-organs for temperature); 49, 1897, 462-468; and the long monograph on pressure and pain (includes discussion of end-organs), *Abhdl. d. kgl. sächs. Gesellsch. d. Wiss. zu Leipzig, math.-phys. Cl.*, 23, 1896, 169-266; or the concise summary in his *Vorlesungen über Physiologie*, 1904, 308-326.

Nafe's Theory

For Nafe's introspective study of the similarities and confusions of tactual data, see J. P. Nafe, The psychology of felt experience, *Amer. J. Psychol.*, 39, 1927, 367-389. For Titchener's "touch pyramid," see Nafe, *op. cit.*, 384-387; E. B. Titchener, *ibid.*, 31, 1920, 213f.

For Nafe's theory, see his Quantitative theory of feeling, *J. Gen. Psychol.*, 2, 1929, 199-211; The sense of feeling, *Foundations of Experimental Psychology*, 1929, 392-

406. Both these expositions are marred by an attempt to make it appear that the traditional theory (von Frey's) has been accepted by psychologists, presumably for a century, because of the weight of Johannes Müller's dictum about specific nerve-energies. Blix in 1883 is a more plausible date than Müller in 1838, and it is probable that the complacent assurance about von Frey's theory has existed mostly in elementary textbooks. Perhaps Nafe will correct this defect and also clear up his somewhat obscure exposition in a revised chapter in the forthcoming second edition of the *Foundations, op. cit.*

In calling his theory a "quantitative theory of feeling," Nafe implies that other theories of quality are not quantitative. The distinction is almost too fine to be observed. Of course, Müller's phrase, "specific energies of nerves," implied the existence of five kinds (qualities) of energies within the five kinds of nerves; but this qualitative view was already giving way to the spot-in-the-brain theory of quality when Blix was writing. *Specific energies* came to mean *specific cortical loci.* Hence the theory of cutaneous quality has always been a quantitative theory unless one thinks of cerebral localization as qualitative and not quantitative—perhaps because the significant loci are discrete and not continuous. For instance, the present author thinks of his entire book as being, in Nafe's sense, a quantitative theory of consciousness. A physiology of consciousness would have, in the present day, to be quantitative in order to be physiology.

Cutaneous Receptors

On the functioning of undifferentiated free nerve-endings in all cutaneous sensibility, see K. M. Dallenbach, Temperature spots and end-organs, *Amer. J. Psychol.*, 39, 1927, 402-427. In *ibid.*, 41, 1929, 344, Dallenbach gives the references to the others who have made the direct histological examination of temperature 'spots': Donaldson, 1885; Goldscheider, 1886 (a thorough study, see his *Gesammelte Abhandlungen*, 1898, I, 219-249); Haggqvist, 1913; Pendleton, 1928. There can be no doubt that von Frey's correlations of sense-organ with temperature spot must be dismissed completely.

On the other hand, as the text points out, there may be invisible differentiation, as we believe that there must be among the retinal cones. Moreover, according to the argument of the text, the crucial case is the differentiation between warmth (or cold) and pressure, since warmth and cold may need the same receptor, and pain may come from 'summation.' Apparently not less than two, nor more than four, kinds of receptors are needed by current theory. In the light of these remarks it becomes interesting to note that histologists have distinguished among the cutaneous nervous structures in a way that might indicate the required differentiation. There are (1) the terminal ramifications between the columnar cells of the epithelium (von

Frey's free endings), (2) the hederiform endings of Ranvier in the
epithelium, especially near the
sweat-ducts, endings that have flat-
tened leaflike enlargements at their
terminations but that nevertheless
closely resemble the terminal ramifications, (3) a reticulum beneath
the epithelium, with the fibers
dividing and anastomosing, without
its being clear whether or not there
is a direct connection with the
endings in the epithelium, and (4)
other hederiform endings (von Frey
said "free endings") well below the
epithelium about the hair-follicles.
See E. A. Schäfer, in *Quain's Elements of Anatomy*, II, i, 1912, 273-
276. There is, however, no need to
press this slight histological evidence into a theory.

Since this text was written Hoagland has reported experiments that
indicate the existence in the skin
of the frog of two kinds of receptors and two corresponding patterns of the current of action. See
H. Hoagland, Specific afferent impulses and cutaneous sensibility,
J. Gen. Psychol., 6, 1932, 276-
295.

On pain as "common sensation,"
see the long discussion of C. S.
Sherrington, in E. A. Schäfer's
Text-book of Physiology, II, 1900,
965-1001 (cf. esp. 998f. on pain as
summation). This exposition shows
how uncertainly experts accepted
the four-modality view of cutaneous
sensibility in 1900. On cutaneous
summation, see also Goldscheider,
op. cit., 397-432.

Chapter 7

THE ORGANIZATION OF CONSCIOUSNESS

THE study of the physiology of the conscious dimensions makes it clear that the fundamental problem of psychology is organization. If we supposed that the discussion of intensity, extensity, protensity and quality would, in each case, resolve itself into a choice among simple hypotheses, we now see that we were mistaken. The problems of extensity are almost entirely problems of spatial organization. The theory of protensity must be a theory of temporal organization that also involves space. Even intensity cannot be regarded simply as neural frequency, for it forces us to consider the total effect of many frequencies in many fibers and the possibility of some kind of summation before they can be effective. And quality—once the theory of minute cerebral centers is abandoned—leads us into the most elaborate theories.

The preceding chapters have implied that all conscious distinctions are discriminative, that consciousness is, broadly speaking, discrimination. Such a view implies that all 'knowledge' is potentially spatial in a physiological sense, that is to say, the awareness of a conscious difference can be reduced to a selection (discrimination) between two reactions and their spatially distinct efferent paths. Hence the afferent correlates of the conscious dimensions have always to be translatable into physiological spatial specificity. It is no wonder then that the supposedly simple problems of the conscious dimensions require an appeal to intricate principles of organization, since they all have to be reduced finally to a common denominator of spatial differentiation. In a certain sense we are looking for a 'place theory' of every dimension.

Nevertheless there are other levels of organization to be considered in psychology. The dimensional problems give us the organizations of perception. Although these organizations are not simple, they are clearly primary; and upon this primary perceptual level other levels depend. Memory is a topic that raises questions about higher organizations in time, and attention is a topic that raises questions about higher organizations in simultaneity. Intelligence is another term that would seem to require an organizational or integrative account for itself. And there are, of course, many other topics which a thoroughgoing psychology would have to consider. However, it would be futile to attempt to extend the scope of this book to the limits of psychology. There are too many flaws in our psychophysiology of perception for us to employ it yet awhile as a foundation for the psychophysiology of the 'higher' mental processes. In this chapter we shall limit ourselves, without any attempt at completeness, to those implications about attention, learning and intelligence, which are immediately appropriate as consequences of the four preceding chapters.

Intelligence

There has been so much talk about intelligence and so many definitions of it that it requires temerity to use the word. However, we can delimit the term sufficiently to serve us in the present context without penetrating deeply into controversial matters.

In psychology the term *intelligence* has come to mean a common factor in intellectual activity. Intelligence is common to all persons, but varies amongst them in degree. It is common to a very large number of seemingly disparate intellectual activities but varies amongst the activities in degree. The most intelligent persons do better than their fellows in the acts that require the most intelligence. Spearman's method of the 'tetrad-difference' is a statistical way of analyzing out such a common factor, and the method indicates the epistemological nature of intelligence. Intelligence comes into reality at a high level of inference. It is not at all the kind of entity that could be regarded as given immediately in experience.

We have first to consider the relation of intelligence to the speed of mental activity. Mental activity always takes time, but the same accomplishment may take different times for different persons. The rate of mental work would bear to human accomplishment the sort of relationship that intelligence bears, and *rate* is the sort of factor that intelligence is. The plausibility of equating intelligence to speed is increased when one reflects that most intelligence tests are speed tests. Time is one measure of animal intelligence in the maze or for the puzzle-box. The usual intelligence test of persons is made against time, and it can be said of the all-or-none tests, where time is irrelevant, that they are simply poor measures since the time required is always minimal or infinite. This point becomes clearer when we see that all-or-none tests for children may be speed tests for adults. What, for example, is the opposite of *impecunious?* That is an all-or-none test for those who do not know the word, but a speed test among well educated English-speaking adults. It seems so plausible that intelligence might be the rate of mental activity. However, the evidence seems to preclude so simple a definition. The range of consciousness would seem to be the fundamental variant in differences of intelligence. Time comes into the picture, but only secondarily because a limited range slows down the total flow of consciousness. This point is elaborated in the notes (pp. 213f.).

If intelligence is not fundamentally the rate of mental

activity, it must be whatever else appears in intelligence tests. The obvious alternative to speed in the tests is 'correctness.' The all-or-none tests are tests in which the response is either right or wrong. All the tests, in so far as they are not measures of the rate of activity, are measures of the capacity of the subject to be right. Whatever could the physiology of 'correctness' be like?

Well, correctness is plainly a relationship. A response is correct if it bears a particular relation to some preëstablished criterion of truth. *Opulent* is the opposite of *impecunious* if that is the way the English language is. '*A*' is the opposite of '*a*' if such is the rule of the game; otherwise it is not. The rules of right-and-wrong for persons are very apt to be social and cultural, and human intelligence has for this reason come to be regarded as essentially social and usually verbal. With rats the rules of right-and-wrong are alimentary; the correct act is the act that gets the food.

One possibility is that intelligence may reduce to the capacity to acquire these conventional relationships, and there is every evidence that persons who have acquired many correct responses also acquire new ones easily. In such a definition we should be equating intelligence to aptitude for learning. The intelligence of the rat in the maze is measured by his ease in learning, and the intelligent rat is the 'learned' rat. The intelligence of persons in verbal tests is measured by their present facility, which depends upon the ease with which they learned in the past. It is a plausible view, but it seems possible to go further.

Learning itself involves discrimination, discrimination between 'right' and 'wrong.' The rat in the simple maze discriminates the right path from the wrong, if he learns. The rat in the temporal maze, in learning to go around the block twice to the right before turning to the left, must discriminate the second trip around to the right from the first. The human subject in the verbal test is very often discriminating among confusing possibilities and has certainly acquired his present knowledge by discrimination. Stern's classical definition of intelligence as the "general ability of an individual consciously to adjust his thinking to new requirements" implies discrimination as the essential ground. *Discrimination* might in our definition be a substitute for *learning*.

However, recent psychology has been tending to emphasize insight as a condition of learning. The indication is that, given insight into a situation, learning may be instantaneous. The reason that learning ordinarily takes time and repetition is that complete insight is dependent upon trial-and-error for its achievement or that the task is so large that insight into part of it occurs at the expense of insight into other parts—a phenomenon usually called 'interference.' However, insight is the organization of discrimination, and on this view learning becomes dependent upon discrimination.

There is no need for us actually to arrive at a formal definition of intelligence. It is quite enough if it becomes apparent that what is ordinarily called 'intelligence' is so closely related to discriminative insight that the measure of the latter would have similar if not identical significance with the measure of the former. Now let us turn to the physiological problem.

Lashley, as we have seen (pp. 103-105), measured the intelligence of rats by the rate at which they learned a maze. He showed that the entire cerebral cortex is involved in such intelligent activity. The destruction of part of the cortex reduces this kind of intelligence; the reduction is proportional to the amount destroyed; the various parts are equipotential with one another, for the destruction of any one is no more effective than the destruction of any other; the projection areas are equipotential for intelligence with other regions of the cortex, and intelligence is thus dependent upon the mass action of the cortex. *The more the better* is the rule of the cortex for intelligence.

The preceding chapters have indicated how relatively complex must be the organizations involved in the simplest sensory perceptions. Obviously the complications must be many times multiplied in the intelligent acts of the learning of the maze by the discrimination of the right path to the food. Any one who has attempted to describe in introspection the process of solving a puzzle realizes the persistent complexity of learning by trial-and-error and also the elaborateness of the flash of insight which may terminate the learning. It is, therefore, not particularly remarkable that such organizations should need all of the cortex in order to realize themselves. The law of mass action is a most probable principle; it is the principle of equipotentiality that is difficult to understand.

When some of the cortex is destroyed, presumably the general pattern of organization can be maintained, but the differentiation is reduced. Hence the capacity for discrimination is diminished. The rule seems to be that differentiation takes up space and time. Reduce the amount of the available cortex and some differentiation is crowded out, unless there is more time into which it can be 'squeezed.' See Fig. 17. In the animal world the size of the brain seems to follow a definite average law in proportion to the size of the body, and it has been held that the more intelligent animals are those whose brain weights exceed this general average, and conversely for weak-minded animals. The inference is that, the more intelligent a person, the larger should be his brain. However, there may easily be individual and phylogenetic differences in functional differentiability that are independent of mere amount of tissue.

There is nothing very new about this conception. It was really an idea of this sort that led Henry Head and his

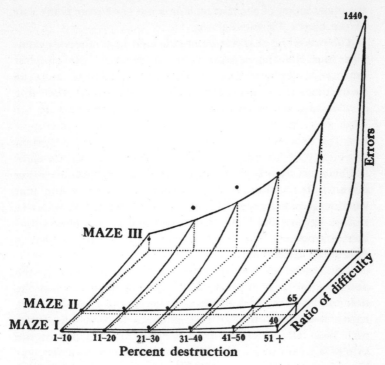

FIG. 17

LASHLEY'S FUNCTION FOR MASS ACTION IN LEARNING THE MAZE

Relation between extent of cerebral lesion, difficulty of problem to be learned, and number of errors in learning. Mazes I, II and III are spaced proportionally to their difficulty for normal rats. The abscissae are the percentages of destruction of the cerebral cortex. The function shows how errors increase with difficulty of maze and also with diminution of available cerebral tissue. Thus the function also shows the relation of cerebral mass to complexity of maze. If a horizontal plane cut the surface at a height for some given number of errors, then the line of intersection between the plane and the surface is a function which shows the amount of cerebral tissue required for any given difficulty of maze, in order that the maze shall be learned with only the given number of errors.

associates to coin the word *epicritic* for the higher (*epi*) discriminatory (*critic*) functions. Head used the word at first only for the higher differentiating class of cutaneous sensations, but Rivers employed it in its general meaning. The functions of the cortex can be regarded as epicritic, and, the more cortex there is, the more critical they can be. We must develop this conception further in the following section.

Attention

There has been so much controversy about what attention is and is not, about whether its laws are true or not, and whether they are properly laws of attention, that one is apt to lose sight of the truth that there really is a fundamental fact of attention. The fact of attention is that consciousness is limited. Attention to one 'thing' requires inattention to others. If you are paying attention to the old lady in the pew in front of you, presumably you are not paying attention to the sermon. Patting your head rapidly with your right hand interferes with stroking your stomach slowly with your left. When the hidden donkey in the puzzle picture is discovered, the donkey appears but the original picture blurs out. The range of attention, we say, is limited.

We soon find, however, that we cannot formulate the principle of limited range without taking account of mental organization. We can attend simultaneously to the old lady and the preacher, if we begin to notice that she nods with approval whenever the preacher raises his voice in denunciation. It is not nearly so hard to learn to pat one's head rapidly with one hand while rubbing one's stomach slowly with the other as it is to learn to operate an automobile. One may be able to see the donkey and the picture at the same time if he becomes interested in how parts of the one are also parts of the other. However, there is no proof that the range of attention is enlarged in these cases. We may have a reduction of conscious content by analysis or by habituation. When the old lady and preacher get organized into a single unit of her-response-to-his-emphasis, there is less of each of them in the field of attention than when either was there alone. The simultaneous patting and rubbing depends upon habituation; it is easy to begin to rub the stomach voluntarily after the patting of the head has become so automatic that it will continue without attention. It is plain that we must resort to some sort of measurement if we are to understand the fact of limited range.

The rapid exposures of tachistoscopic experiments show us that range is not abruptly limited—or at least that adventitious factors prevent the appearance of abrupt limits in experimentation. However, this view has not always been held. For a long time the range of attention was supposed to be six. Six what? Six "items" or six "units," where a group of units becomes a unit. The nature of the unit was never clear. The "six" came in part from Sir William Hamilton, who threw marbles on the floor, estimated quickly the number at a glance, and concluded that six was the maximal correct number. A much more instructive early experiment is that of the logician, Jevons. He performed Hamilton's experiment by estimating at a glance the number of beans thrown into a box. The percentages of correct rapid estimates for various numbers of beans is as follows:

No. beans...	3	4	5	6	7	8	9	10	11	12	13	14	15
Per cent correct ...	100	100	96	82	73	56	62	43	38	42	23	28	18

Jevons thought that these results meant that between four and five beans could be crowded into attention at once. A more accurate statement of Jevons's results would be that, although four beans can always get into attention, fifteen beans may be apprehended in almost one case out of five. Perhaps eighteen is the range; eighteen beans might under ordinary circumstances sometimes be correctly estimated. It is, however, much better to appeal to statistical constants. Fernberger has computed the limen at 10.28 beans, *i.e.*, the number of beans that should, under Jevons's conditions, be as often correctly apprehended as not.

Now it is extremely probable that the only way in which Jevons could estimate a dozen beans correctly was by seeing that they formed groups or patterns; that is to say, the range depended upon the organization of the material within it (as Hamilton had already pointed out). Here Cattell's classical tachistoscopic experiments are in point, though they are not so complete as Jevons's. Cattell exposed lines, letters, short words, and short sentences very briefly to observers, whose correct apprehensions can be stated in percentages. While these data do not admit of careful statistical treatment, it is approximately true that the observers could correctly apprehend 6.3 lines, 4.5 letters, 2.2 words, and one short sentence as often as not. For the purposes of discussion let us neglect the decimals and consider the integers for these limens. Investigation shows that the average letter contained about three lines, that the average word contained about five letters, and that the sort of sentence correctly apprehended contained about six short words. Hence Cattell's ranges of attention may be said to be:

$$6 \text{ lines}$$
$$4 \text{ letters} = 12 \text{ lines}$$
$$2 \text{ words} = 10 \text{ letters} = 30 \text{ lines}$$
$$1 \text{ sentence} = 6 \text{ words} = 30 \text{ letters} = 90 \text{ lines}$$

In other words, you can perceive (as often as not) six isolated lines, twelve lines organized as letters, thirty lines organized as words, and ninety lines organized into a printed sentence. On the other hand, there is with increasing complexity of organization a loss in the number of units; you cannot get tachistoscopically as many sentences as words, nor as many words as letters, nor as many letters as lines. Such a table, reliably worked out, gives the complete results of the range of apprehension for any material in any formal system of organization.

However, it is not necessarily to be supposed that the range of attention is really increased by organization. Expose for a tenth of a second ten consonants in a row, and the observer will seldom perceive them all correctly. Then expose the ten letters of the word PHILOSOPHY, and the observer will seem to perceive them all correctly; he 'knows what the word was.' Then expose the word PHYCHOLOBY, and the observer will almost inevitably say that he has perceived the word PSYCHOLOGY. Hence it appears that being correct is not necessarily a measure of differentiation in perception. The reason why one perceives in a tenth of a second PHILOSOPHY correctly and fails for PDWMGSFRBT, is that not all of PHILOSOPHY is perceived; a part of it stands for the whole because the whole is familiar. Thus it is that habituation makes an analysis, and a part functions in attention for a whole.

In the foregoing discussion is contained the key to the psychology of thought and the 'higher mental processes.' What distinguishes thought from perception and idea is symbolism, the functioning under habituation of a part for a whole. Many such wholes, reduced each to a part, can form a new whole within the limits of attention, and then a part can come to function for this new whole and combine with other parts, and so on to *superiora* of any degree in the functional heirarchy of symbolism. James Mill remarked on the complexity of the idea of a house, composed, as he supposed, of the ideas of brick, mortar, rafter, nail, glass, wood, and so forth; and then he raised the climactic question as to how many ideas there would be "in the idea called Every Thing." Well, here is the answer to James Mill's question. We can think of Every Thing, not by thinking of every different thing at once, but by thinking that symbol which implicates everything, both logically and psychologically, because the implications can become explicit if there is any later requirement that they should be.

It is not difficult to see how this conception of attention accords with the principle of mass action and with the discriminational theory of intelligence set forth in the preceding section of this chapter. Attention is limited in range by the amount of tissue available for functional differentiation in the perceptual or ideational whole. *At a given moment* a person can think of so much and no more because he has only just so much brain with which to do the thinking.

There are other problems of attention besides the problem of range, and we may now consider briefly three of these.

(1) Attention is dependent upon compulsory *conditions*. Sudden intense stimulation conditions attention. Moving objects are apt to be attended to when the rest of the perceptual field is still. The novel among the familiar or the familiar among the novel is generally singled out for attention. The observer may be predetermined by abiding interest or transient intent to notice one sort of object and to neglect others. What is wanted and wanting here is some reasonable conception of a facilitation that will show why a loud noise, a pretty face, and an interesting idea have more command than their neutral competitors upon the neural activity that leads to discriminatory response.

(2) When attention is caught it does not *endure* long. The classical experiments on the fluctuation of faint stimuli and of reversible perspectives are not relevant, as modern psychology realizes, but nevertheless there are rapid and con-

stant changes in consciousness. Critical introspection immediately reveals this fact. James had it in mind when, com-
bating atomistic elementarism, he described the stream of
thought. The Wundtians had it in mind when they called the
mental element a *process*. It is obvious in any perception.
Geissler's observers, who 'attended' for two or three minutes to a weight on the skin, are shown by their printed
introspections to have been continuously varying the contents of consciousness as they pertained to the weight.

Among the experiments, Pillsbury's is undoubtedly most
in point. He had the observer attend to a tiny ink dot. This
stimulus was so simple that there was not much chance for
the attention to wander within the field that means the stimulus. (Of course, there is always the chance that the observer
will become inattentive by attending to the idea that he is
attending.) The observer was to release a key when his attention left the dot and to press it again when attention
returned to the dot. However, he could not very well release
the key when his attention left the dot, because he was in-
structed to attend to the dot and thus it would have been
just as easy to keep on attending as to release the key. But
he could generally, although not always, manage to signal
when his attention returned from wandering. The alternations of attention thus constituted a very elementary splitting
of the personality, and these double alternations were on the
average from one to two seconds long. Since some of the
alternations were missed by the observers and all were
double, Pillsbury concluded that a "wave of attention"
might be as short as half a second. Undoubtedly half a
second indicates the order of the rapidity with which one
conscious organization gives place to another, or with which
a single phase of one organization gives place to a discriminably subsequent phase of the same totality.

There is no conventional physiological approach to this

problem. The times of action currents and of synaptic delays are much shorter than any interval that can be discriminated in introspection. Presumably Pillsbury's times represent, not the elementary phases of the physiological event, but its differentiation in respect of the reaction that introspection is.

(3) There remains the question of the *degree* of attention. The two-level theory is conventional. It assumes two degrees of clearness in consciousness, a focus and a margin. Focal consciousness is readily reportable as compared with marginal consciousness. In fact there is some systematic difficulty in showing how the obscure marginal contexts are ever described, since clearness seems to be a condition of description. The confusion in general discussion comes about principally because attention is sometimes regarded as a sensory matter to be described and sometimes as a cognitive process of description. We cannot, however, examine this controversy here. This book presents a cognitive theory of all sensory process. It is clear that it could offer no account of attention other than a cognitive one. Attention is reportability. It is limited by the range of the organizations that underlie report. It is determined by whatever determines these organized neural activities. It is ever changing with the change of such organization under the physiological laws of rapid growth and decay.

Whatever conscious content can be easily reported is focal and available to introspection. What cannot be reported at all is unconscious. Is there some intermediate level, some marginal zone? There ought to be, or how did the two-level theory ever gain credence? Introspection might answer this question, but it never has. There has been too little introspection upon introspection for introspection's good. It is possible that dichotomy of reportabilities might be formed between those reports that come quickly, unreflectively and without doubt, and those that come slowly, reflectively, and with low assurance. Introspection upon the margin of consciousness often is the focal apprehension of a sensory process that is a surrogate for an immediately past marginal process. (Cf. pp. 225-227.) Thus it is possible that the two levels may turn out to represent two degrees of immediacy in report.

Learning

The criticism by Gestalt psychologists of the conventional hypotheses of learning and memory has tended to result in the substitution of the concept of organization for the concept of association. Perhaps we have only dismissed Peter and elected Paul, for after all association has to be considered as both simultaneous and successive, and most of the experiments upon association show that the kind of organization involved is not a simple bonding together of distinct units but a complex integration of a whole. Nevertheless, Gestalt psychology has done a service in stressing the simultaneity of associative organization. Wundt also stressed simultaneity, but the emphasis has lain on successivity because so much of learning and memory is verbal and language is serial. Obviously learning must consist in the formation of an organized differentiated pattern to which selective response can be made.

The dependence of such organizations upon the principle of mass action and upon the amount of available nervous tissue has been the principal topic of discussion in the present chapter. Discrimination is the only possible evidence of learning, but discrimination is also a measure of attention and the capacity for discrimination furnishes a practicable conception of intelligence. We are talking about only one thing when we discuss learning, attention, and intelligence. Old-fashioned psychology expressed this idea by saying that attention is a necessary condition of learning and that the capacity to learn is dependent upon intelligence.

The fundamental problem of *memory* is, of course, presented in the question: How do these organizations persist? To this question there is not even a wise speculative answer available at the present time. The reflexological theory is that the learned patterns persist in space by new connections or lowered resistances established in learning. The concept of the equipotentiality of regions is opposed to this view. It means that a localized pattern is not localized in any place, and that, if it is crowded into a smaller region, no spatially complete part of it is cut off, but differentiation is 'squeezed out' of all of it, while the gross form remains. Since we do not know how such a pattern is formed, we cannot guess how it might persist. The answer to the one question is probably the answer to the other. In perception the pattern of organization, of which the central localization is irrelevant, exists potentially and strictly localized in the peripheral excitation. If we knew more about how these potentialities are realized, we might be able to guess how they can persist.

Thus it seems that the answer to the problem of memory ought to come by a further knowledge of the laws of learning, and here the outlook is a little more promising. At least we now know that there are two possible kinds of organizational complication; one that helps learning and memory and one that hinders.

What sort of things help or facilitate learning?

(1) One of the simplest aids is *rhythmical grouping*, either free or predetermined. Learning a disconnected series of items—a list of nonsense syllables or the alphabet—is difficult because no organization is given in the materials. All learners, if left to themselves, throw such a series into a rhythm. Every one of us probably now uses for the alphabet the rhythm that he imposed upon the series of letters in childhood. In the formal experiments of the learning of lists of nonsense syllables, rhythms are predetermined by the experimenter; the simple trochee is generally used. It is found

that these tiny groups are better organized in memory than the larger units that contain them; the subject learns to complete the metrical foot before he learns to connect the feet. In longer materials the organization is perfected first for the beginning, next for the end, and last for the middle. (Hence we make indices of the *first* lines of poems, not the last lines nor the middle lines.) Still longer materials, like a poem of several stanzas, may show this positional function holding for the entire material with the same function for each of the parts superimposed upon it. While we see here differences in the effectiveness of groupings, all grouping of this sort is an aid to learning. It is generally believed that verbal material cannot be learned at all if rhythmization is completely prevented.

(2) There are conditions under which an apparently discursive loose organization gets itself structured into a whole, every part benefiting from its participation in the whole. For instance, one of Ebbinghaus's classical experiments consisted in the learning of various series of nonsense syllables, and then subsequently the learning of new series made up of syllables which had been next but one to each other in the first learning. Thus, if a part of an originally learned series had included TOB-VID-RUD-ZEN-DAK, the new series to be learned would include TOB-RUD-DAK, and—this is the point of the experiment—the new series would be learned more quickly than the original series, showing that the first organization was not completely altered in the second. This result is especially interesting because in many other cases the putting of old terms into new relationships is more difficult than the original establishment of the first relationships. However, it may be added that Ebbinghaus found a saving, not only for syllables next but one to each other, but also for syllables next but two, next but three, next but seven, and next but one backwards.

(3) It can be said that the advantage of the first learning in the foregoing experiment was partially transferred to the second learning because the syllables became familiar or were impressed in the first learning. Be that as it may, it is plain that *familiarity with language* renders words a much easier material for learning than nonsense. For a number of years the author has had the members of his introductory course in psychology read aloud twelve times in chorus the following list of ten nonsense syllables:

MAX   PIB   GUK   TOV   DEG   ZID   FEP   BOT   RUZ   WAM

After the twelfth reading the list is taken away and the students immediately write down all the syllables they can remember. Although exceptional persons may get all ten syllables correct or only two correct, the average for the class is every year not far from 65 per cent correct (14 out of 19 cases lie between 62 per cent and 68 per cent). Then the same experiment is performed with these words:

FUN   SIR   TOP   WED   NAG   BOX   DAY   HEM   PUT   RIB

Here the majority get all ten words correct and few persons fail to get as many as eight right. The averages approximate 93 per cent correct (ranging from 92 per cent to 94 per cent for 16 of the 19 cases). What makes the words so much easier to learn than the nonsense syllables? Well, for one thing, the words are already knit up as units. In a three-letter word FU might be combined with N or R but hardly anything else. Moreover, it is true that some of the chance connections may be already partly learned, as it were. Most undergraduates see at once a meaningful relationship between WED and NAG, although the author intended no such connection when he made out the series. It is clear that a great deal of the transfer of learning from the general knowledge of language to the learning of a list of words is due to the fact that language provides some ready-made parts which can be assembled for the new structure. Furthermore, it seems probable that we are justified in supposing that, in addition to this principle, there is an attentional economy for the familiar material of language. We have seen that PHYCHOLOBY, presented tachistoscopically for a fraction of a second, can function in perception for PSYCHOLOGY. Perhaps familiarity means the reduction of a unit of organization. Perhaps words make less demand upon cerebral space than do nonsense syllables. Then—this is the natural conclusion of this line of thought—perhaps the learning of a material consists simply in its reduction so that the organization required for mastery can be accommodated within the available mass of tissue in the available time.

(4) *Mnemotechnical* systems supply various illustrations of the way in which meaningful relationships aid learning. Often these useful devices are bizarre or silly, like the relationship of WED to NAG already referred to. However, it is of great interest to note that the spatial relation is remarkably effective for learning as compared with other apparently adventitious relationships. How often one recalls where on a 'right' or a 'left' page a sought-for statement occurred without the least idea as to what page or what chapter contained it. Four unrelated objects can be quickly impressed on memory by imaging them, one on each of the four walls of a room. After that the memorizer stands in memory in the room and picks the images off of the walls. If consciousness is discrimination and if discrimination ultimately reduces to spatial differentiation, one can see how spatial difference would be peculiarly effective for learning. Its importance is what one might expect from the law of mass action.

(5) The mnemotechnical systems provide us only with examples of absurd effective relationships. We must go to

the normal process of education to find the sensible *meaningful relationships* in use. Here it can be said that a very great part of the educational problem is to make learning sensible. Learning is easy when there is *insight*. The occurrence of insight seems to imply an elaboration of differentiation. Introspection, however, reveals no such elaboration. The 'flash of insight' is a reduced consciousness with surprisingly little content. The subsequent rationalization of the insight is apt to be a difficult process which results in an elaborate logical structure, but logical organization is not psychological.

(6) As we have noted elsewhere in this chapter (pp. 214f.), learning is aided by the *active participation* of the learner. Passive mechanical reading of a list of syllables might never get them learned. However, it is not possible to separate activation from insight. The two are correlated. Insight seems usually to occur under an active attitude, and it is probable that the dynamic factor in the conditions of learning is nothing other than that which favors attentive differentiation.

Now we may turn to the other side of the picture. What sort of things inhibit learning or interfere with memory?

(1) It is plain that interference may come when one learning directly *contradicts* an established learning. It is hard to break a habit in order to form a new one. If one has always called a person Kate, it is hard to learn to say Katharine. If a man has been frightened by a snake, it is hard for him to learn to be friendly with one. So Bergström showed that when a person had learned to sort cards into boxes, each card to a specified box, it was harder to learn to sort the cards when the specifications were changed and the same cards had to be differently distributed among the boxes. The second learning was harder than the first because it included an unlearning of the first. However, we do not always

get this kind of interference when we expect it. There is very little difference between Bergström's experiment which shows interference and the experiment of Ebbinghaus, cited above, which shows facilitation. Ebbinghaus, in linking up alternate syllables, had to unlink the syllables that were already connected. Why was the second learning easier than the first? Bergström used the same boxes and cards. Why was his second learning harder? There is really no answer to this dilemma at present. We say that Ebbinghaus found 'positive transfer,' and that Bergström, under similar but not identical conditions, found 'negative transfer.' We must assume that positive transfer means that the first learning accomplishes some of the organization required in the second, and that negative transfer means that the first learning establishes relationships that must be 'unorganized' before the second pattern can be formed. The most plausible conclusion that can be formed at present from our knowledge of the transfer of learning from one task to another is that any two learnings would involve elements of both positive and negative transfer, and what we measure in an experiment is the algebraic sum. We know so little about the detailed analysis of learnings that we should not at present expect to be able to predict in a given case whether transfer would be positive, zero, or negative. And the researches on transfer give exactly this result—an unpredictable distribution of positive, zero, and negative transfers.

(2) *Retroactive inhibition* is the term applied to a loss in the effects of learning due to the mental activity that follows learning. It is generally believed that interference of this sort is greatest for similar activities. After learning nonsense syllables it would be worst for memory to learn more nonsense syllables, and reading the newspaper would hardly interfere at all. To play tennis after studying one lesson and before starting the next should lead to little inter-

ference. There are many demonstrable cases of retroactive inhibition. However, it is plain that there may be positive cases of retroaction, where the subsequent mental activity serves to fix the original learning. If, after learning a list of syllables, the learner then uses the same syllables in some other way, like identifying them when they are individually presented in a tachistoscope, then there might be a positive retroactive transfer from the subsequent impression of the earlier learning.

(3) The experiment of Jenkins and Dallenbach shows that a mental state which gives very little retroactive inhibition—perhaps none at all—is *sleep*. They determined the forgetting functions of two observers for an eight-hour period after learning. The curves where the interval was filled with normal waking activities show the usual continuous decrease from 100 per cent immediately after learning to about 30 per cent after two hours and about 10 per cent after eight hours. They also performed the experiment with the observers sleeping in the laboratory after learning and being waked for testing. In this experiment memory fell off from 100 per cent to about 55 per cent in the first two hours and then remained constant for the subsequent six hours. It is a possible inference from this experiment that all forgetting is due to retroactive inhibition, that forgetting is slowed but not abolished in the early hours of [light?] sleep, and that it is abolished in the later hours of [deep?] sleep. The princess who slept soundly for a hundred years would remember perfectly when she awoke—much to Ebbinghaus's embarrassment, for he thought that the mere lapse of time was enough to let impressions fade away.

(4) It is more difficult to learn a long list of nonsense syllables than a short one. Ebbinghaus learned a list of twelve syllables in sixteen repetitions, but required thirty repetitions to learn a list of sixteen syllables. This means that,

at the rate of one syllable per second, the twelve-syllable list took 192 seconds (sixteen seconds per syllable) and the sixteen syllable list 480 seconds (thirty seconds per syllable.) The time is almost doubled when the amount of the material is increased by only a third. We can call this a case of interference similar to the interference in retroactive inhibition; the added syllables interfere with the learning of the others. However, we can also see that we have a situation similar to the one depicted in Fig. 17 (p. 193). That figure shows, for any size of cerebrum, the disproportionately increasing retardation of learning as the number of cul-de-sacs in the maze (difficulty of the maze) increases. When difficulty of material is measured by the number of syllables in a list we have the same sort of function. Presumably it is hard to learn a long list because the parts of the organization have to be somewhat reduced before the entire pattern can be squeezed into the brain. If this inference is true, we should expect to find that a very few syllables could be learned at once without the repetitions necessary to get the pattern reduced to practicable size, and, as every psychologist knows, the empirical finding is just that. Six or seven nonsense syllables are learned within a single repetition. "Because," we say, "they fall within the range of attention." However, the range of attention is the range of the cerebrum (so our argument runs); you can reduce the range of attention with a scalpel.

(5) Most psychologists believe that the first repetition of a material has the greatest effect upon learning, and that successive repetitions yield successively diminishing returns in the establishment of learning. Certainly the function is true when learning is measured by the proportion of the total material that is completely mastered after any given number of repetitions. Now the only case where more than one repetition is needed (as we have just been saying) is

when the material is too large to come immediately within the range of attention. The effect of successive repetitions must be to 'reduce' the material to the scope of a single organization. We have seen that insight furnishes an example of such reduction, and also that any orderly attentional fixation may act in that way. The implication is that reduction is implicit in organization, that organization is a process, and that as soon as a unit gets organized it bulks less large in the competition for cerebral space. The organization that is the learning is built up gradually piecemeal. Every learning experiment, in which the complete material does not pop into complete mastery at the same moment, shows this fact. Thus it happens that the principles of chance come to apply. The first repetition organizes some part of the total material—any part, for it is all unorganized to start with (let us say). The second repetition is at a disadvantage. It needs to effect the organization and reduction of a new portion, and it is largely wasted if it is simply a mere repetition of the physiological events of the first repetition. When the total material is almost learned the chances of bringing just the right part into organization on a succeeding repetition are minimal, and on the average the repetitions just before complete mastery are least effective because they have the least chance of being effective. This point is a difficult one and is discussed further in the notes (pp. 219f.).

This discussion of the conditions favorable and unfavorable to learning has been long and involved. However, the picture that it implies for cerebral events is fairly simple. Let us see if we can delineate it quickly.

Learning is a matter of the establishment of neural organization, and depends largely upon the cerebral cortex. It is a mass action and its rate is a function of the amount of cerebral tissue available. Simple organizations that lie within the adequacy of the cortex (within the 'range of attention') may be learned instantaneously in a single repetition. Larger materials that cannot at once be comprehended within a single 'attention' are organized piecemeal. Organization results in the functional 'reduction' of any material, so that parts after reduction can be comprehended in a single 'attention,' when before reduction they would have crowded each other out. Some of this reduction is due to surrogation, the substitution of a symbolic part for a whole. It is not at all clear as to whether all reduction is a matter of symbolic surrogation. Reduction is illustrated by the difference for organization of a brand new nonsense syllable and a familiar monosyllabic word. At any rate learning is a process of getting into a single consciousness more than it would originally hold.

Consciousness is continuous, except perhaps for sleep. When we ask how different conscious activities affect each other in memory, we find that there is sometimes mutual aid which may be due to community of organized units, and that there is sometimes opposition which may be due to the incompatibility of organized units. The facts of positive and negative transfer and of positive and negative retroactive transfer follow from these assumptions. Forgetting may be merely negative retroaction. The difficulty of learning long materials may be due to mutual interference among the parts.

It seems quite possible that learning occurs at an elementary level in accordance with an all-or-none principle. The instantaneous learning with insight would thus illustrate all simple learning. However, when the material transcends the range of consciousness, as it perpetually does in the integrations which life demands, then the larger organization is formed piecemeal, and the all-or-none character of learning is obscured by the fact that the total organization is achieved gradually. We talk about the degree of mastery of a material as if it might be all half-learned, when the indubitable fact is that it is half all-learned. All-or-none functions that are subject to adventitious variations can thus be translated into intermediate degrees by applying principles of probability to them, as indeed is habitually and consciously done in psychophysics.

There is probably little hope that the psychophysiology of the 'higher mental processes' will ultimately be worked out with the relative simplicity of the generalizations of the present chapter. On the other hand, this picture seems to the author to be a reasonable presentation of the more sophisticated thought of the present day, if that thought is to be brought into relation with some law of mass action of the cerebral cortex. The establishment or the refutation or, if necessary, the modification of this law is of primary importance to psychology at the present time.

Notes

A very simple way to think of the nature of consciousness is to realize that introspection is discriminative and that a discrimination can be reduced to a differential response, *e.g.*, the right forefinger can be flexed for event *A* and extended for event *not-A*. Thus *A* must excite the path for finger-flexion, and any other event must excite another path. The two efferent paths are spatially distinct at the periphery. It is in this sense that the text remarks that all theories of dimensional discrimination ultimately reduce to 'place theories.'

Intelligence

For definitions of intelligence and discussion of the concept of intelligence, see the symposium by thirteen distinguished authors, Intelligence and its measurement, *J. Educ. Psychol.*, 12, 1921, 123-141, 195-216. There is an excellent summary in R. Pintner, *Intelligence Testing*, 2d ed., 1931, 3-102, esp. 45-102. See also C. Spearman, *The Abilities of Man*, 1927, 1-135. For Stern's classical definition, see W. Stern, *Psychological Methods of Testing Intelligence*, trans. 1914, 1-5. Spearman originally thought of intelligence as discrimination; cf. his "General intelligence," objectively determined and measured, *Amer. J. Psychol.*, 15, 1904, 201-292; but the view fell into disrepute when it was found that simple sensory individual differences do not show high correlations with intellectual differences. The position of the present text differs from this older notion in that it assumes that total organizations, involving the entire cerebral cortex, are much larger and more complex than the simpler organizations which are involved in sensory discriminations and which are limited either to a part of the cortex or to a subcortical region.

Intelligence as Speed

The text finds inadequate the conception of intelligence as the rate of mental work (speed), although the present author has previously made just that suggestion. See H. Peak and E. G. Boring, The factor of speed in intelligence, *J. Exper. Psychol.*, 9, 1926, 71-94, where it is noted that variation in rate of nervous conduction would be a common factor. The change of view in the present text is a shift of emphasis from a time-theory of intelligence to a space-theory. However, there is nothing in the new theory that supposes that time cannot do duty for space. See Fig. 17. The rats learned even Maze III when they had only half a cortex, but it took longer. The total differentiation is spatial-temporal. The author is inclined to stress the dimension of simultaneity in considering intelligence, because a man (or a rat) has only one life to live, there is only so much time, and it is interesting to see how individuals vary in respect of accomplishment within the same period of time. The symmetrical point of view would be expressed as follows: *A* was more intelligent than *B* because, with an equal

capacity for mental accomplishment in any given time, he lived twice as long. *A* had two minutes for every minute that *B* had. It is obvious therefore that a 'space-theory' of intelligence must also be a 'time-theory.' The more that can be got into a space at one time the sooner is that space free for still more. Traffic is *speeded* up by increasing the *width* of the highway.

In this way the space-theory is a time-theory, because, the more space available, the less time required. The rate of mental work is speeded up by the greater range of attention, since consciousness must be occupied. However, space is the primary variable under consideration and rate is secondary and dependent upon space. It is for this reason that the present view is not truly a 'speed-theory.'

However, the ease with which the argument about simultaneity and time assumes paradoxical form suggests that some of the inconsistencies of this literature may be explained by the fact that every definition of intelligence in terms of range must also imply a definition in relation to time, and conversely. For some of the contradictory views of intelligence, based upon different kinds of investigation, see R. A. McFarland, The rôle of speed in mental ability, *Psychol. Bull.*, 25, 1928, 595-612; M. Kennedy, Speed as a personality trait, *J. Soc. Psychol.*, 1, 1930, 287-290.

A 'speed' test measures the rate of mental work. *Power* in physical science means *the rate of work.* Psychologists have used the word *power* for the tests that are all-or-none in their results and are therefore not *speed* tests. It is too bad, such an exact reversal of the meaning of a word.

Intelligence as Discrimination

It really matters very little to the argument of this chapter whether or not psychologists will accept a definition of intelligence as capacity for that differentiation which leads to discrimination. It is plain that many intellectual and seemingly intelligent activities are dependent upon discrimination, that is to say, upon the precise differentiation of elaborate organizations. The author thinks that the word intelligence is appropriate in such a context, but he will have no quarrel with those who want a different word. In this connection it is convenient to note that common language also allies *intelligence* to *discrimination;* cf. "the intelligent person," "the discriminating person."

The references to Lashley's work have been given in chap. 4, pp. 123f. Lashley's correlation between amount of cortical destruction and errors made in learning a difficult maze is 0.86 ± 0.03. Simpler mazes give lower correlations, the simpler the lower, presumably because they are not so complex as to require all of the cortex for the mental activity of the discriminating rat. Moreover, the correlations between amount of destruction and time of learning are lower than when errors are used instead of time as the measure, presumably because the number of errors is an approxi-

mately correct measure of the discriminatory capacity which depends upon mass cerebral action, whereas time is only indirectly a measure because errors take time. See, on these particular matters, Fig. 17 and K. S. Lashley, *Brain Mechanisms and Intelligence,* 1929, 61-67, 70-75.

For the modern view of the relation of the size of the brain to intelligence, see L. Lapicque, Le poids du cerveau et l'intelligence, *J. de psychol.,* 19, 1922, 5-23. Lapicque determined the average formula; a constant, $k = $ brain weight/(body weight)$^{0.56}$. For men this becomes $k = 1360/(6600)^{0.56} = 2.73$. For women, $k = 1220/(5400)^{0.56} = 2.74$. Since k is practically the same in both cases (with a single point of difference for courtesy), the two sexes should be equally intelligent; but k is not the same in different animal species.

Intelligence as Insight

The argument that all learning is insightful must be indirect. The term *insight* was first introduced by Köhler to describe the way in which apes, after failing to solve a problem, seem suddenly to become aware of the relationships involved, to solve the problem, and then to remain master of the new situation. See W. Köhler, *The Mentality of Apes,* trans. 1925. Yerkes has sought to give such insight meaning in terms of objectively definite criteria. See R. M. Yerkes, The mind of a gorilla, *Genet. Psychol. Monog.,* 2, 1927, 155-168, esp. 156. Köhler extended the concept greatly in *Gestalt Psychology*, 1929, 349-394, but it is pp. 269-300 in his book that make the argument against frequency of contiguity as the theory of learning and (by implication) in favor of insight. On this point, see also K. Koffka, *The Growth of the Mind*, trans. 1924, 143-237, esp. 179-230. McDougall had the same point in mind in saying that learning must be purposeful. Cf. W. Mc-Dougall, *Outline of Psychology*, 1923, 302-304. The actual ground for these views lies in the experiments that show that mechanical repetition is not nearly so good as a condition of learning as frequent efforts at recitation, and the further indication that sheer passive repetition may not give rise to any memory at all. In this matter see W. Poppelreuter, Nachweis der Unzweckmässigkeit die gebräuchlichen Assoziationsexperimente mit sinnlosen Silben nach dem Erlernungs- und Trefferverfahren zur exakten Gewinnung elementarer Reproduktionsgesetze zu verwenden, *Zsch. f. Psychol.*, 61, 1912, 1-24; A. Kühn, Ueber Einprägung durch Lesen und durch Rezitieren, *ibid.*, 68, 1914, 396-481; A. I. Gates, Recitation as a factor in memorizing, *Arch. of Psychol.*, 1917, no. 40; M. Smith and W. McDougall, Some experiments in learning and retention, *Brit. J. Psychol.*, 10, 1920, 199-210; B. Zeigarnik, Das Behalten erledigter und unerledigter Handlungen, *Psychol. Forsch.*, 9, 1927, 1-85. Cf. also E. L. Thorndike, *Human Learning*, 1931. Zeigarnik writes in Lewin's series and represents Lewin's conception

that activation is necessary for learning; see in general K. Lewin's introduction to his Untersuchungen zur Handlungs- und Affekt-Psychologie, *ibid.*, 7, 1926, 294-385. One interesting thing about this literature is the way in which *insight* and *motivation* become interchangeable, a relationship that, when recognized, does much to enlighten the problem.

Rats, left free and unfed in a maze, become 'familiar' with the maze, so that later, when food is supplied at the food-box, they learn rapidly and may overtake in their learning the rats who are learning the maze with regular feeding in each trial at the food-box. See H. C. Blodgett, The effect of the introduction of reward upon the maze performance of rats, *Univ. Calif. Publ. Psychol.*, 4, 1929, 113-134; cf. E. C. Tolman, *Purposive Behavior in Animals and Men*, 1932, 48-50. Tolman uses the term *inventive ideation* for *insight;* for his general discussion of it, see *ibid.*, 219-232. On another way in which familiarity with the maze reduced the time of learning it, see M. F. Washburn, *The Animal Mind*, 3d ed., 1926, 275.

Attention

Sir William Hamilton tells of throwing the marbles in his *Lectures on Metaphysics and Logic*, 1859, I, 176f. For W. S. Jevons and the beans, see his The power of numerical discrimination, *Nature*, 3, 1871, 281f. For J. McK. Cattell's tachistoscopic experiments, see his Ueber die Trägheit der Netzhaut und des Sehcentrums, *Philos. Stud.*, 3, 1885, 121-127, esp. 126. J. P. Hylan, The distribution of attention, *Psychol. Rev.*, 10, 1903, 498ff., esp. 499, summarizes Cattell and puts him into a little table. S. W. Fernberger, A preliminary study of the range of visual apprehension, *Amer. J. Psychol.*, 32, 1921, 121-133, reviews this literature, cites other discussions of it, computes the relative frequencies and the limen for Jevons, and reports a modernized form of the experiment, the first with accurate psychophysical technique for the determinations of range. Fernberger's conditions were chosen to prevent grouping; hence it is necessary to go back to Cattell for the data of the text. The limens for Cattell's observations were approximated roughly by drawing similar ogives through his plotted data. Their exact values are unimportant.

James Mill comments on the complexity of thought in his *Analysis of the Human Mind*, 1829 (or the 1869 ed.), I, chap. 3, par. 12.

For William James on the stream of thought, see his *Principles of Psychology*, 1890, I, 224-290. It is a nice question as to just how the word *process* (*Vorgang*) came to be used as designating the elementary mental material. Wundt tended to speak of *elements*, *impressions*, *sensations*, *perceptions*, *ideas*, although the term *mental process* was no longer unusual for him in 1902. Meanwhile O. Külpe, *Grundriss der Psychologie*, 1893, cf. sect. 4, had made the phrase *mental process* equivalent to *mental element*, and E. B. Titchener, *Outline of Psychology*, 1896, sect. 3, followed Külpe. It seems fair to say that the process-nature of consciousness, the fact of change and flux, has been pretty clearly recognized since about 1890.

For prolonged attention, which certainly included internal fluctuations, see L. R. Geissler, Fluctuations of attention to cutaneous stimuli, *Amer. J. Psychol.*, 18, 1907, 309-321. W. B. Pillsbury's experiment is "Fluctuations of attention" and the refractory period, *J. Philos.*, 10, 1913, 181-185, a more important publication than its length suggests.

On the general psychophysiology of attention, see L. T. Troland, *Principles of Psychophysiology*, III, 1932, 137-154.

Attention as Cognition

We must note here very briefly the principal historical outlines of the psychology of attention, since they have been ignored in the text. The distinction between the sensory and the cognitive, the structural and the functional, aspects of attention was not sharply drawn in the nineteenth century. Wundt's *Apperception* has retained a cognitive meaning even after Wundt defined it in structural terms. *Aufmerksamkeit* has to be kept from its literal meaning of *noticeability*. Wundt saw this distinction and pointed out the corresponding kinds of clearness, *Klarheit* and *Deutlichkeit*, but the experiments did not cleave to the one or the other, and we shall not be far from the truth if we say that the psychology of 1900 tended to assume that *Klarheit* is the essential condition of *Deutlichkeit*, and thus to investigate the one by means of the other. It was Titchener who was most distinctly to draw the line between structural, sensory process and functional, cognitive meaning, and he tried to rescue *attention* from the functional household by establishing it in his own psychological ménage as an attribute of sensation called *clearness* (1908, 1910) or *vividness* (1915) or *attensity* (1924). Thus for the doctrine of attention as sensory, attributive clearness, see E. B. Titchener, *Lectures on the Elementary Psychology of Feeling and Attention*, 1908, esp. 171-206. However, Titchener still managed to have something to say about the old laws of attention: range, fluctuation, levels, accommodation. It remained for K. M. Dallenbach, Attributive vs. cognitive clearness, *J. Exper. Psychol.*, 3, 1920, 183-230, to take the logical step of separating the facts under the heads of attributive clearness and cognitive clearness. This act of justice resulted in stripping attributive clearness of most of its facts and giving them to cognitive clearness. Dallenbach, of course, believed that attributive clearness still held title to the word *attention*, although (it would seem) to little else. The present author believes that it is in the public interest to take the term *attention* for cognitive clearness. It is not even clear that the legal title does not lie thus. Meanwhile sensory clearness has ceased for

Titchener and Dallenbach to be attributive and has become metamorphosed into *attensity*, a fifth dimension of consciousness. Whether attensity is a necessary dimension of consciousness, future study will show. At present it seems to have little systematic significance. Nothing serious happens to a system of psychology if the concept of attensity as a structural, sensory, descriptive category is left out.

It should now be obvious why the text makes no distinction between such phrases as *range of apprehension* and *range of attention*. Fernberger used the former phrase in 1921 (*op. cit.*) because of Dallenbach's distinction in 1920 (*op. cit.*).

The discussion in the text of the degree of attention should make it clear why elsewhere there has been no attempt to make the Wundtian distinction between the range of attention (focus, *Blickpunkt*) and the range of consciousness (focus and margin, *Blickfeld*).

Learning

On the necessity of rhythmization for learning, see G. E. Müller and F. Schumann, Experimentelle Beiträge zur Untersuchung des Gedächtnisses, *Zsch. f. Psychol.*, 6, 1894, 280-285; M. K. Smith, Rhythmus und Arbeit, *Philos. Stud.*, 16, 1900, 197-277, esp. 254-265. On the importance of the kind of rhythm, see Müller and Schumann, 156-158. For the demonstration that the 'bonds' are stronger within rhythmical feet than between them, see *idem*, 106-130. Briefly on these matters, see also E. Meumann, *Psychology of Learning*, trans. 1913, 263f. On the effect of position within a material (the comparison of the beginning, middle, and end) and some other of these matters, see H. Ebbinghaus, *Grundzüge der Psychologie*, I, 1905, 653-656. Some of the examples of the text are taken from H. Ebbinghaus's classical *Ueber das Gedächtnis*, 1885, Eng. trans. as *Memory*, 1913. For the way in which learning in a series transfers to the connections between remote members, see his chap. 9. For the way in which the work of learning increases rapidly with the increase in the length of a series, see his chap. 5.

For the author's class-demonstration of the difference between learning sense and nonsense syllables, see his discussion of the matter when eleven (instead of nineteen) cases were available, E. G. Boring, Demonstrational experiments in memory, *Amer. J. Psychol.*, 40, 1928, 513f.

For the experiment that shows negative transfer through interference, see J. A. Bergström, Experiments upon physiological memory by means of the interference of associations, *Amer. J. Psychol.*, 5, 1893, 356-369; An experimental study of some of the conditions of mental activity, *ibid.*, 6, 1894, 267-273; The relation of interference to the practice effect of association, *ibid.*, 6, 1894, 433-442. In this connection see the general discussion by W. S. Hunter in *Foundations of Experimental Psychology*, 1929, 611-615. Hunter points to A. T. Poffenberger, The influence of im-

provements in one simple mental process upon other related processes, *J. Educ. Psychol.*, 6, 1915, 459-474, as showing how positive, negative, and zero transfers occur in different cases with seeming adventitiousness.

The fundamental idea that retroactive transfer may be negative or positive and that the maximum of retroactive inhibition would occur when the second task is neither enough like the first to reënforce it nor enough different to leave it unaffected, is due to E. S. Robinson, The similarity factor in retroaction, *Amer. J. Psychol.*, 39, 1927, 297-312. On retroaction in general, see Hunter, *op. cit.*, 599-605, and the many references there cited.

For the striking and dramatic experiment upon retention during sleep, see J. G. Jenkins and K. M. Dallenbach, Obliviscence during sleep and waking, *Amer. J. Psychol.*, 35, 1924, 605-612.

The classical experiment on the value of successive repetitions is P. Ephrussi, Experimentelle Beiträge zur Lehre vom Gedächtnis, *Zsch. f. Psychol.*, 37, 1905, 222-234, who worked with the method of promptings. Of course the measurement of degree of mastery by counting the frequency of promptings is an example of the kind of function where an all-or-none event is translated into degrees by an appeal to the relative frequency of its occurrence. *Vide infra*, the next section of these notes.

The examples of insight in the apes and higher mammals generally involve the chance apprehension, after delay, of the essentials among a tremendous complexity of potential perceptual data. If conditions could be made so simple that attention is practically limited to essentials, and if these essentials are well within the range of attention, then one might expect learning (organization, insight) to occur instantaneously on the first perceptual relating of the essentials. This seems to be exactly what B. F. Skinner has found with the rat in experiments which are peculiarly relevant to the content of the present chapter. See B. F. Skinner, On the rate of formation of a conditioned reflex, *J. Gen. Psychol.*, 7, 1932, 274-286. See also the section of these notes, *Intelligence as Insight, supra.*

Frequency Functions

A separate note is in order on the power of frequency functions apparently to transform phenomena that occur under the all-or-none principle into phenomena of variable and measurable degree.

The phenomena of both sensation and memory follow the all-or-none principle. The memorial reproduction of an item of a material either occurs or it does not. No item in itself is observed as half-remembered. It has been conventional to speak of 'strong subliminal associations,' as if subliminal associations were of various strengths, but the inference as to subliminal strength is indirect and uncertain. So also a sensation either occurs from stimulation or it does not. If it does not, it has no demonstrable intensity. Fechner talked about negative (subliminal) degrees of intensity, but that is not

good psychology to-day. Above the limen we can sense degrees of intensity, but introspection cannot directly measure these degrees. We are forced to comparison, and there again we meet an all-or-none principle. Either we can observe a difference or we cannot. Introspection as to the amount of difference is not quantitatively reliable.

In either case the psychologist resorts to a function of relative frequencies. He plots against degree of stimulation the frequency with which the all-or-none sensation is all there, and he gets what in psychophysics is called a psychometric function. The limen, the point where one might suppose that the *none* would change to the *all*, becomes sophisticatedly the point which yields 50 per cent of none and 50 per cent of all, *i.e.*, the point where sensation is as likely as not to occur. On either side of the limen the psychometric function progresses toward the limits of 100 per cent and 0 per cent, with its precipitancy measured by the coefficient of precision. It seems then as if we were measuring something about a sensation, but actually we are measuring only the probability that a sensation will occur under the given conditions. A statement of probability is empirically only a statement of relative frequency of occurrence, and a frequency cannot apply to a single sensation. A frequency function of this sort can apply only to an average; it pertains to a group and is meaningless as applied to a single case.

(The chances of drawing any particular card from a pack are

only 1 in 52. If one draws, one always draws a particular card. Hence in drawing it is the improbable that always happens. This paradox arises from the faulty language of the theory of probabilities, which makes it appear that a probability inheres in a single event, whereas it can pertain only to the total group to which the event belongs.)

The memory experiments resemble the psychophysical ones. The all-or-none of reproduction is transformed into degree by considering relative frequency within a total material. When a material is said to be half-learned, we mean that half of it is all-learned, not that all of it is half-learned. Thus all measures of degree of mastery hold only on the average for materials where chance variation occurs.

The chief point of this dissertation for the present text is to show that learning may proceed essentially by the all-or-none principle in spite of the fact that degree of mastery is measurable in large materials. It is possible that Ebbinghaus's fundamental law of frequency is a statistical artifact. The function of many repetitions for learning may simply be that of providing enough chances for all parts of a large material finally to get within the 'range of attention' and be organized into a stable totality.

There is also a very much more general significance to this property of a frequency function. In biology and psychology we are constantly finding functions that have limiting maxima and minima.

The minimum is often the zero of something. The maximum is generally the all of something. Such a function is a frequency function. It is a matter of common scientific intuition that functions in approaching limits of this sort approach gradually, curving toward the boundaries, as if asymptotic. By what right can such a form be anticipated? Well, it is the natural form of a frequency function. Discrete quantal phenomena of the all-or-none kind, when affected by chance variation and translated into relative frequencies, give not only continuous curves, but also functions that are smoothed out toward their limits, so that the function does not even show an abrupt change of direction. The important point to note here is that we are not facing a fundamental biological fact in noting the absence of abrupt changes in biological functions where we might expect them. We are presented rather with the logical fact that the smooth function does not indicate continuity in the phenomenon, but is an artifact of the method of measurement, an artifact that is often missed because conventional scientific language applies to the individual phenomenon what actually pertains only to the massed group.

The reader can see how the theory of probabilities will change the discreteness of sensory events (or of coin tosses) into continuities by consulting various texts on probabilities and least squares, or E. G. Boring, A chart of the psychometric function, *Amer. J. Psychol.*, 28, 1917, 465-470.

Chapter 8

THE NATURE OF CONSCIOUSNESS

IT is now time for us to consider some of the more general implications about consciousness to be derived from the preceding chapters. Our approach to these larger theoretical issues has been, in a sense, inductive. At any rate, except for the necessary preliminary considerations of the first chapter, we have done our best to consider the particular before the general. Of the dimensions of consciousness intensity comes nearest to being able to stand on its own feet, although it must lean nevertheless a little upon extensity. The problems of extensity lead us somewhat further into the conventional assumptions of psychophysiology. Protensity raises a difficulty for the theory of simple correspondence between conscious and neural duration, and seems to force us to a view of consciousness as discrimination or reaction. Quality, the unexplained dimension, has largely to be speculated about, but such speculation tends to reënforce this same view, which may be called a relational theory of consciousness. The problems of the larger organizations of consciousness take us into a consideration of the parts played by local and momentary differentiation under the limitations set by the nervous system. This procedure may be convincing, but it involves a dangerous subtlety. By lending a speck of credulity here, by endorsing a very small assumption there, we may find ourselves rationally bankrupt. Hence we must now sum up the account of consciousness in order to see whether our new enterprise is sound.

The Relational Theory of Consciousness

There are two ways of expressing the view of the nature of consciousness that has been developed in this book. One way—an old-fashioned way—is to say that (1) *the data of consciousness are meanings.* A newer way, and a way that is free of the hackneyed connotations of the word *meaning,* is to say that (2) *consciousness exists as relations and exists only in the sense that relations exist.* We must not at this point ask what the relations are *between;* the answer to that question comes later (pp. 229-233).

The reason that the first statement reduces to the second is that *a meaning is a relation.* The philosophers tell us this, but it is also evident in psychology. Titchener's context theory of meaning, if sufficiently extended, meets with very general acceptance. Titchener held that a sensation in itself is meaningless, but that it receives a meaning when another sensation or image accrues to it. The perceived face lacks meaning until the name comes. The protozoan must turn from the light, before the light can have a meaning for the protozoan. Meaning is given by the addition of a "context" to a "core." Although Titchener would have repudiated the suggestion, it is nevertheless plain that this 'context' is a 'reaction' to the 'core.' The context theory of meaning is essentially a reaction theory. Moreover, Titchener held that in very familiar perceptions meaning may become unconscious and be carried only by nervous processes. The test of such a meaning can only be behavioral. The child in learning to play the piano has a very conscious context, when *b* is to be flatted, of what he is to do with his finger; but, when he has become a little skilled, he no longer remembers consciously even the key in which he plays, and his finger takes care of itself. At first he knows consciously that *b* is to be flatted; later he knows the same thing unconsciously;

in either case he has, Titchener would have said, the same meaning; in either case, we may add, the meaning is there because a discriminatory reaction is there. Titchener said that it takes two mental processes to make a conscious meaning. We are saying that it takes two events in relation to make a meaning. Absurdly paradoxical as it may seem, the context theory of meaning, fathered by Titchener, makes behaviorism, which Titchener excommunicated, the true cognitive psychology. Meaning is response.

However, to say that meaning is response is not to say that consciousness is meaning. The traditional view is quite otherwise. Introspectional psychology up to about 1915 had been formulated in terms of such conscious contents as sensations and images. These contents were supposed in general to exist. They were sometimes called *existential* on this account. When it became clear during the last decade that the conscious contents were only systematic constructs, the emphasis shifted to the phenomena that phenomenological psychology provided. Then it seemed clear that phenomena are given in experience, that they are the existential subject-matter of psychology. Gestalt psychology, it seems, has tended to include with the phenomena many items that Titchener's existential school would have regarded as meanings; however, it gets these 'meanings' into direct experience by robbing them of their relational character. All these matters need concern us only in so far as they show that introspectional psychology, both the Gestalt branch and the 'existential' branch, regards experience as given in its own right within psychology. Phenomenal experience stands on its own feet. It exists and psychology may take it and do what it can with it. Observation—here is the crux of the matter—does not change the observed. To the depreciation of the value of this view the present section of this book is devoted.

We can get some idea of what consciousness is like by

considering the nature of anesthesia. Under complete general anesthesia a person may properly be said to be 'unconscious.' To imagine that he may be conscious and unable to tell of it at the time or to remember it afterward is to formulate a scientifically useless conception of consciousness. We may lay it down as a premise that consciousness is abolished in anesthesia. The dualistic phenomenologist can easily accept this view; the brain is partly thrown out of function and the phenomena do not occur. He need not say why they do not occur, because dualism provides no answer to such a question.

Now let us try to imagine a condition of progressive amnesia in which consciousness is normal but no memory persists for more than a second of time. Some descriptions of the scopolamine syndrome ('twilight sleep') resemble such a state of affairs, but the hypothetical case is sufficient for our purpose. Could we under these circumstances distinguish between the anesthesia and the amnesia? A little consideration shows that we could not. Without memories of a second's duration no introspective report would be possible, nor would there, if the subject had no memory at all of what was immediately past, be any moment at which he would be aware of his own consciousness.

Even when memory is not so drastically affected, we find it hard to assert the existence of consciousness. A person is struck on the head with resulting concussion. He is taken to the hospital and on the way he babbles intelligently and correctly about himself, his name, his address, his occupation, what he was doing when struck. Yet a few minutes later he has no memory at all of his recent conversation, and will go over the same statements again as if they were new. Is such a person at such a time conscious? Presumably we must say, Yes. This person could give an introspection of sorts. His memory is long enough for that. Nevertheless we see that such a 'consciousness' with a very short memory resembles what is sometimes called the 'unconsciousness' of hysterical states and divided personality.

It was once suggested that sleep is not unconsciousness after all, but a state of concentrated attention upon a fatigue sensation. Could we disprove such a theory? Suppose the same sensory phenomenon could occupy the range of consciousness all through the night. Since the sleeper is aware only of his fatigue he will not have been aware of his consciousness. He could not remember the fatigue afterward, for of what could such a memory consist? A mere imaginal reproduction of the fatigue would not date it as having occurred the night before or at any particular time at all. The subject would not even know that the memory was a memory.

All these instances go to show that consciousness actually depends upon memory for our knowledge of it, and that the concept of a consciousness that exists independently of memory is a concept pretty far removed from the actual consciousnesses that enter as subject-matter into scientific psychology. And memory, of course, is relational. It means that an initial term is represented in a subsequent term, which reciprocally implies the first.

The same problem arises in connection with the cognitive function of attention. Years ago Titchener believed that the feelings, pleasantness and unpleasantness, lack, as he put it, the attribute of clearness. He meant that the feelings have nothing to do with attention. They cannot be attended to or attended from. They cannot come into the focus of attention nor stay out. They are neither clear nor obscure. At the same time Titchener believed (he changed both views later) that attention is involved in observation; one attends in order to observe. Suppose Titchener were right about the feelings and about observation. How then could we ever know

about these feelings? Feelings would have to be observed
before they could exist *for psychology*. Moreover, the observation would turn out to consist of a reaction to the feeling in some sort of report or cognitive note-taking.

In all this business we are dealing indirectly with the
old, philosophers' objection to introspective psychology—
that there can be no introspection because the mind alters
itself in observing itself. To introspection consciousness
ought to be introspection, since introspection would always
find the mind introspecting. Psychology undertook to meet
this objection by establishing the doctrine of immediate
experience, a doctrine which amounted, in the opinion of
the present author, to a denial that introspection is a
method, that it accomplishes something. To have experience
is to be aware of it; that is the view of any psychologist,
like Wundt, who emphasizes a distinction between immediate
and mediate experience. However, the having of immediate
experience is a contradiction in terms, for an experience is
already mediate when it is had. A strictly neutral phenomenology encounters this same difficulty. Titchener tried to
avoid the trouble by an appeal to Avenarius's formula; for
him psychology was not immediate experience but experience
got from the psychological point of view. In 1915 he wrote
the formula for psychological method thus:

Introspection = psychological (vivid experience → report)

Experience must be focalized in attention. It must issue in
report. Both the attentive focalization and the reportorial
issuance must occur under the psychological point of view.
In this way Titchener has made for us the formal argument for a relational theory of consciousness, although he
himself undoubtedly would have repudiated the theory.

Titchener's formula is the argument for a relational theory
of consciousness because it includes report. The vivid ex-

perience must be reacted to, if it is to be known. *Report* for Titchener could include all sorts of contexts to the vivid core—a word, a sentence, the pressing of a key, the unexpressed fleeting processes of introspective 'note-taking' as the 'experience' proceeds, a fleeting contextual image that 'carries a meaning' for the introspection. However, Titchener's formula is equally applicable to 'animal introspection,' the process whereby an animal by discriminatory response gives information about his consciousness. The 'experience' occurs; the response to it is the report of it. Titchener would have said: But the animal does not have the psychological point of view. No, but the experimenter has it. The experiment may be so arranged that the response will mean the event to which it is a response. If the introspecting observer can interpret his own conscious reactions for the purposes of introspection, the experimenting observer can similarly interpret the behavioral reactions of a rat who knows nothing at all about scientific psychology.

It might seem that a final appeal in the matter of this relational theory of consciousness ought to be the introspection of introspection. Unfortunately formal descriptions of this sort are lacking, and one is therefore forced to take personal experience seriously, to resort, as it were, to 'armchair' psychology. The author's present convictions about consciousness arose in an introspective experiment in 1921. They have been constantly reënforced since that time. He ventures to set them down here in the belief that others who have extensively attempted to introspect upon introspection will affirm their validity.

The most striking thing about consciousness is its continual flux and change. It is not split up into elements or Gestalten, but is truly as continuous as a stream with eddies and currents and pools. I never perceive any phenomenon as fixed. I am inclined to believe that none is fixed, that change is perfectly continuous; but I am bound to admit that I know only that I do not know that they are fixed. They might persist a little while, but I do not know that they do. How then is it that I perceive this red diamond in the rug? Does it enter consciousness as a sensation, a perception, a Gestalt, a conscious organization, a phenomenon, and linger there, perhaps for a second, while I take note of it for the purposes of subsequent verbal report? Not at all. I never am aware of this or any other conscious datum as being present in mind. To be aware of a conscious datum is to be sure that it has passed. The nearest actual approach to immediate introspection is early retrospection. The experience described, if there is any such, is always just past; the description is present. However, if I ask myself how I know that the description is present, I find myself describing the processes that made up the description; the original describing is past and it is presumably the new description of the description that is present. To find myself thus landed in an infinite regress is to find myself just where I seem to myself to be. Experience itself is at the end of the introspective rainbow. The rainbow may have an end and the end be somewhere; yet I seem never to get to it.

Thus I believe quite firmly in the context theory of meaning, that the accrual of one process to another may establish a meaning. However, my awareness of consciousness or of any conscious phenomenon seems always to be the having of such meanings, not the 'core,' not the 'context,' but the accrual of the context to the core. Such relations inhering in the flux of consciousness seem to me to be just what consciousness can best be said to be.

The phenomenologist and the existentialist will of course not be able to understand this view, any more than I can understand theirs. They will insist that an experience is given, that a phenomenon exists, and that my statement, that they appear to exist only after they have ceased to exist, is absurd. At any given waking moment, they will say, there must be in consciousness something more palpable than the implication of a past event. To such a statement I can only oppose my own 'experience' and the query: What would consciousness seem to be like, if the knowledge of it were always *ex post facto* and the knowledge of the knowledge of it *ex post facto,* and so on? Would not the phenomenologists, with consciousnesses of this sort, still be able to hold to their belief in immediate experience? I think they would.

It is now apparent that the final appeal as to the nature of consciousness will not be to the introspection of introspection if the results are like those of the three preceding paragraphs. Introspection in such a case yields not fact but conviction, and conviction unsupported by any external test is not enough. What are we to do? In the author's opinion, we are to appeal to physiology. It is enough if, in the present section of this book, we have found the relational view of consciousness plausible, a reasonable alternative to the static view of mental elements and their big cousins, the Gestalten. Perhaps the discovery of a relational physiology will help us to make a choice.

Relational Physiology

From one point of view the central nervous system is a relational organ. It exists for integration. Its primary function is coördination. Its typical relation is reaction, the stimulus-response relation. Response is necessarily specific and thus it is discriminatory. In terms of any one of these words could a cognitive systematic psychology be written: *reaction, response, reflex, discrimination, differentiation.* They all imply a specific relation.

Fundamentally, of course, this relation is the relation of cause and effect. A movement becomes a response when it is known as the effect of a stimulus; a physical event at a receptor becomes a stimulus when it is known as the cause of a response. This typical relation can be applied to any terms of the causal sequence. A conscious event may be regarded as the 'response' to a stimulus or as the 'stimulus' to some movement. Ultimately it is the business of psychology to knit up the successive phases of the total integration that is bounded, on the one hand, by stimulus and, on the other, by response.

It is important for us to realize that causal events are not necessarily serially linear. Any simple causal sequence is almost certain to be an oversimplification of the facts. Psychophysiological events constitute dynamic wholes. Nevertheless they proceed in time, and for convenience they can be divided into phases, each of which is predetermined by its prior conditions. These phases need not be distinct in any actual fashion. Analysis is only the tool of description. Nevertheless it is a necessary tool, and actual total events can be best understood as parts in relation. The relational theory of the nervous system is fundamentally the deterministic, causal theory.

However, the psychologist's interest centers especially in those relations of the nervous system that are subject to change in the lifetime of the individual. Consciousness is concerned with awareness and the acquisition of knowledge. Learning has been considered rightly as the criterion of consciousness in the animal scale. Knowledge is properly that which has been learned. Do I and that stone each *know* where the earth is, because when released in air we fall toward it? Hardly, for this reaction is not learned. Well, then, do I know that that object is green because I have 'a green sensation'? Yes, but only if I have *learned* that the green sensation is green and that it means that object. It is here that the thesis of this book differs from existential psychology. There is not, so the author argues, a green sensation except as a learned relation, a specific response to a specific stimulus. The color-blind person, for instance, has less specificity of response. Moreover, it has often been said that if you see red where I see green, and conversely, both of us with consistent systems, obverse and reverse, then we should never be able to find out that there is any difference between our seeings—a statement that says that phenomena exist for science only as they are reported, and that the report depends on learning.

Now it is plain that most learning is localized in the brain and that a great deal of that learning depends upon the cerebral cortex. Since consciousness depends upon learning, we can now see why it is that consciousness is ordinarily supposed to be localized in the brain. It has been said that, when consciousness is represented by the relation of stimulus-response, it is localized in the peripheral as well as the central nervous system, and also in the receptor and the muscle. It is true that a particular consciousness would be abolished by peripheral extirpation; it takes an eye to see. However, the peripheral relationships are for the most part fixed and not subject to ready establishment and disestablishment, to learning and unlearning. For this reason they are not nearly so important to us as the central types of organization, which are formed readily and, therefore, come under the more usual criterion of consciousness. It is for this reason and for this reason alone that we think of consciousness as localized in the brain. It is in the brain that the discriminatory reactions, which make up consciousness, are formed and have to be studied. The peripheral relationships, being approximately fixed, can be left out of account when the formation of new relations is the business in hand. The correct road is chosen at the fork of the roads; nothing else counts in the choice. So discrimination belongs in the brain where it is finally determined.

We come out with the same conclusion if we stress attention, instead of learning, as the criterion of consciousness. Consciousness is attentive; attention is selective; consciousness is selective. Attention and consciousness are almost synonyms, and selection is the fundamental principle of both. However, the selection is a selection among the various peripheral excitations which are available for central organization. The selection is central and mostly of the brain. In this sense too we have a reason for speaking of consciousness as localized in the brain.

Of course, we have argued in the preceding chapter that the selection (which is attention) is the ground of learning. It is no wonder that these two criteria yield the same conclusions.

We are now in a position to revert to the problem of the preceding section of this chapter. There we argued that a relational theory of consciousness is plausible on introspective grounds, and then turned to physiology. Now we see that the relational view of the brain is the only view that could interest psychologists. Does not this functional picture of the brain lead us in the same instant to abandon dualism and to embrace the relational theory of consciousness?

Forty years ago, when psychophysical parallelism was well entrenched, psychologists found themselves in possession of a picture of mind as made up of ideas connected by associations, and a picture of the brain as made up of neurons connected by synapses. The parallelism was inescapable, that there should be an idea for every cell and an association for every synapse. The law of exercise was built up on this assumption.

Now we know that this psychology was wrong and we are not any too sure of the physiology. Our conception of the nervous system is not nearly so simple, but we can be sure that its function is relational. The traditional view of consciousness is self-contradictory. It gives us mental processes which do not proceed, dynamic integrations which get stabilized as Gestalten or forms, sensations which do not exist. We have—most distressingly of all—meanings which are relations between terms which are not there. What is the matter?

The author offers as the solution for all these difficulties the relational theory of consciousness. Let the realities be neural. We know the general nature of the neural events which yield the relations that concern us. If consciousness seems to introspection to be relational and yet we cannot find the terms that are related, it is because the terms are really neural. The relational theory of consciousness means merely that introspection reveals the relational nature of some of the events in the central nervous system, where selection, learning, and discrimination occur. We have at last a causal theory of mind, in which the events of consciousness lend themselves to insightful relationships with other events. The gap between mind and body, never more than feebly bridged by isomorphism, disappears when we form our realities on this pattern.

The Dimensions of Consciousness

Now that the significance of our liberation from the tyranny of an impracticable parallelism is clear, we may examine again briefly the conclusions which we have reached in respect of the dimensions of consciousness which are ultimately physical realities. These paragraphs will thus constitute a brief—dogmatic—resumé of our entire excursion into psychophysiological theory.

Psychology is interested in the *specific causal relationships,* which represent the reaction of the individual to his environment, and which are seen most typically in the relation of *stimulus-response.* It is especially concerned with such relationships when they are established (or disestablished) in the lifetime of the individual as the result of *organization* under *attentive selection.* These relations are imperfectly indicated in introspection, and they may be said to constitute consciousness.

In this way consciousness is seen to be *cognitive,* or noetic, to have to do with knowledge and meanings. Consciousness is *discriminative,* and discrimination is the symptom of consciousness. Discrimination depends upon *differentiation,* and we must look in the nervous system for the necessary differentiation. Consciousness is *localized in the brain* in the sense that discriminative specificity originates there within the differentiated field that may be imposed by the periphery.

Discrimination may ultimately be *spatial,* for introspection can be reduced to a selection between two neural paths. It is not clear that verbal introspection is thus spatially differentiated, but there is also no evidence that it is not. Spatial differentiation in the mechanism of introspection implies spatial differentiation in the immediately preceding neural events. In this sense all the dimensions of consciousness require 'place theories.' On the other hand, there is no simple set of formulas that appears any longer to be adequate for the ways in which peripheral events are transformed into central organizations.

Intensity at the more peripheral levels seems to imply total excitation in limited space and time, that is to say, both frequency of impulses in a single fiber and the total number of fibers are concerned. We infer then, not exactly to a space-time summation in the brain before the consciousness can issue, but to a single resultant that is a function of the total excitation in a limited number of adjacent fibers in a limited time.

Extensity seems to require for its comprehension spatial organization in the brain. There can be no exact projection, but there must be a correspondence of spatial orders, except where perception is inadequate or illusory. Quite possibly this organization is sometimes tridimensional. Apparently its form is more definitely determined by the stimulus than its size, and its locus is only roughly guaranteed by the stimulus within certain approximate limitations of projection.

Protensity, the durational dimension, must be represented by some terminal event that is specific for the lapsed time and capable of producing a discriminative response. A relativistic interpretation of temporal perception robs it of much of its mystery.

Quality, however, presents the greatest difficulties of all. For difference of modality we have obviously the place theory; the projection paths of the five senses are different, and discrimination is a differential of this gross spatial differentiation. Within the modalities we are faced with puzzles. In respect of hearing, the author inclines to a frequency theory of pitch because of its subsumptive power. In vision it seems as if nothing but a place theory of three elements could satisfy the requirements of color. The author argues that cutaneous should resemble visual sensibility in this regard.

Discrimination, as we have just noted, depends on selection. The limited *range of consciousness* seems to be one of the most obvious facts of psychology, and Lashley's work now makes it reasonable to suppose that this limitation is, at least in part, dependent upon the amount of tissue available for the differentiated organization of nervous processes. *Intelligence,* under the law of mass action, may be the amount of spatial differentiation possible, as might be expected if all discrimination must at some stage of reaction be spatial differentiation. It can be supposed that selection for organization occurs in part by chance from among the available possibilities, but that organization for *memory* is immediate upon selection. The law of frequency would thus be a statistical artifact that explains the way in which a complex material is drawn piecemeal into the range of consciousness. However, this view will work only if it is supplemented by some conception of a way in which organized material is reduced upon organization, so that it makes less claim upon the range of consciousness. Such a reduction may come about by surrogation in which a part functions for the whole, but it is by no means certain that no other kind of reduction can occur.

Just as we have been saying that there is in introspection no distinguishable line between observation and inference, so in science in general the demarcation is never clear. If we have been led in these chapters into highly inferential speculation about the nervous system, we have yielded only to the necessity for defining the boundaries of the fundamental problems of a physiological psychology and for ridding ourselves of the mystery of an *unanschauliche Bewusstheit*, the impalpable and imponderable consciousness that will not lock horns with physical reality or honestly assume a part in a closed causal system. If it seems paradoxical that such elaborate means should be required to achieve simplicity, that so much sophistication should be needed to justify common sense, we must remember that the inertia of human thought is so great that not even a minor simplification is ever the result of a simple process.

Notes

The present chapter is such a continuation of the first chapter of this book as is now possible after the intervening six chapters.

Consciousness as Relational

For E. B. Titchener and the context theory of meaning, see his *Lectures on the Experimental Psychology of the Thought-Processes,* 1909, 174-184; *A Text-book of Psychology,* 1910, 364-373; also the further references cited in E. G. Boring, *A History of Experimental Psychology,* 1929, 429 (cf. the discussion of Titchener, 408-412). C. C. Pratt, *The Meaning of Music,*

1931, 8-28, has a lucid discussion of meaning, which, however, avoids the issue that anything that is called meaning ought to be essentially relational. On the other hand, behaviorism has generally dealt with meaning without saying so, and the present author has tried to make it clear that behaviorism provides the psychology of meaning *par excellence*. Cf. Boring, *op. cit.*, 588, and then see p. 594 for the references. E. C. Tolman's *Purposive Behavior in Animals and Men*, 1932, most explicitly presents this view.

For the idea that sleep represents cerebral hyperemia and perhaps, therefore, a concentrated state of attention, see J. F. Shepard, *The Circulation and Sleep*, 1914, esp. 76-78.

For Titchener's view of feeling as incapable of becoming the object of attention, see his *Lectures on the Elementary Psychology of Feeling and Attention*, 1908, 69-77; or more briefly his *Text-book, op. cit.*, 231f.

The reader will find some preliminary remarks on the problem of introspection in Boring, *op. cit.*, 326-329 (Wundt), 390-392 (Mach, Avenarius, Külpe), and 410-412 (Titchener). Titchener's formula for introspection, quoted in the text, is from his *A Beginner's Psychology*, 1915, 19.

It is Müller and Titchener who discuss, as it were, the introspection of introspection. See G. E. Müller, *Zur Analyse der Gedächtnistätigkeit und des Vorstellungsverlaufes*, I, 1911, 61-176; Titchener, Prolegomena to a study of intro-

spection, *Amer. J. Psychol.*, 23, 1912, 427-448; The schema of introspection, *ibid.*, 485-508. The latter paper of Titchener's summarizes Müller.

The author's convictions about the nature of consciousness were formed when he was an observer at Clark University in an experiment of M. Yokoyama's on the problem of the phenomenal concurrence of different sensory attributes; cf. E. G. Boring, Attribute and sensation, *Amer. J. Psychol.*, 35, 1924, 301-304.

Consciousness and the Brain

The question of the localization of consciousness is really much less important than the question of the localization of interest when consciousness is being considered. Interest is localized in the brain because it is here that the crucial relations lie. For a surprisingly specific view of the localization of consciousness, see L. T. Troland, *Principles of Psychophysiology*, III, 1932, 51-60. For a view that more nearly resembles the exposition of this book, see R. Dodge, *Conditions and Consequences of Human Variability*, 1931, esp. 135-162.

On learning or modifiability of behavior as a criterion of consciousness, see M. F. Washburn, *The Animal Mind*, 1926, 25-33. This discussion also shows how learning as a criterion involves discrimination, and thus selectivity, and thus attention.

There is an increasing tendency to apply Köhler's term, *isomorphism*, to the general correspond-

ence between the orders of phenomenal mind and the orders of
neural body, as if thought space
were neural space, thought time
neural time, thought intensity
neural intensity, and thought quality neural 'what-you-may-call-it.' It
should be clear now that no such
simple correspondence can possibly
be correct. W. Köhler used the
word only for space, but had similar principles for time and for
organization; see his *Gestalt Psychology*, 1929, 61-67.

If this conception of consciousness must be classified among the
conventional theories of the mind-
body relation, then it is an *identity*
theory. It would not be difficult,
however, to substitute for it a
double-aspect theory. The identity
theory has for an advantage the
fact that it avoids easily the traditional habit of regarding conscious
processes as stable and fixed. The
author, however, goes further.
He believes that any correlation
that is perfect in time and also in
space (if the question of localization can be raised at all) is evidence of identity. A double-aspect
theory does not seem to him to be
tenable; or at least the two aspects,
perfectly correlated, must imply the
same reality. Cf. the notes of chap.
I (p. 16).

INDEX OF NAMES

Adrian, E. D., 39, 46, 48f., 53, 58f., 139
Alrutz, S., 34, 182
Alston, J. H., 182
Angell, F., 119
Aristotle, 18, 171
Avenarius, R., 4f., 15, 226, 237

Baird, J. W., 58
Banister, H., 117
Bayliss, W. M., 147
Becher, E., 34
Bell, C., 18, 171
Bentley, M., 85, 117
Benussi, V., 146
Bergström, J. A., 206f., 218
Berkeley, G., 4, 120, 151-153, 155-157, 182
Bernstein, J., 58, 64, 67-70, 73 115f., 125
Blix, M., 33f., 161, 172f., 177, 184f.
Blodgett, H. C., 215
Blumenfeld, W., 120f.
Bolton, T. L., 134f., 146f.
Boring, E. G., 14f., 34, 58f., 115, 117, 121, 125, 146, 182, 184, 213, 218, 220, 236f.
Boring, L. D., 146
Bourdon, B., 32
Bousfield, W. A., 113, 125
Bray, C. W., 50-54, 59, 74, 167
Broca, P., 101
Brues, A. M., 169, 183
Brush, E. N., 132, 146
Bryan, W. L., 32
Burnett, N. C., 182
Bush, W. T., 15

Calkins, M. W., 20, 32
Carlson, A. J., 34
Cattell, J. McK., 196, 215f.
Child, C. M., 60
Curtis, J. N., 35, 146

Cutler, T. H., 121
Cutolo, F., 182

Dallenbach, K. M., 172, 182, 185, 208, 217f.
Descartes, R., 3f. 15
Dessoir, M., 173, 184
Dietze, G., 134f., 146
Dimmick, F. L., 33, 35, 126
Dodge, R., 237
Donaldson, H. H., 185
Dunlap, K., 148

Ebbinghaus, H., 183, 203, 207f., 218, 220
Ephrussi, P., 218

Fechner, G. T., 11f., 19, 70f., 115, 219
Fernberger, S. W., 81, 117, 196, 216f.
Ferree, C. E., 183
Findley, A. E., 35
Forbes, A., 40, 58
Fortuyn, A. E. B. D., 101f., 123
Franz, S. I., 123
Frey, M. v., 32, 172-175, 184-186
Fritsch, G., 101
Fröbes, J., 146

Gahagan, L., 117
Gates, A. I., 214
Geissler, L. R., 199, 216
Goldscheider, A., 33f., 140, 147, 172, 174, 184-186
Graham, C. H., 59
Gray, A. A., 59
Gregg, A., 58
Griffith, C. R., 34
Gundlach, R., 84f., 117

Haggqvist, G., 185
Hall, G. S., 134

Halverson, H. M., 82-84, 116
Hamilton, W., 195f., 215
Hartline, H. K., 59
Head, H., 34, 58, 73, 111, 116, 124f., 192f.
Hecht, S., 45f., 53, 58, 61, 162f., 183
Helmholtz, H. L. F. v., 49, 64, 96, 128, 154, 157, 159-162, 165f., 171f., 182, 184
Henning, H., 26-29, 35
Henri, V., 124
Herbart, J. F., 109
Hering, E., 64f., 162f.
Herrick, C. J., 57, 123
Hillebrand, F., 120
Hitzig, E., 101
Hoagland, H., 58-60, 115, 186
Holt, E. B., 16
Hornbostel, E. M. v., 125
Hume, D., 8, 12, 17f.
Hunt, W. A., 32
Hunter, W. S., 124, 148f., 218
Hylan, J. P., 216

James, W., 18, 129, 147, 199, 216
Jastrow, J., 148
Jenkins, J. G., 208, 218
Jevons, W. S., 195, 215f.

Kant, I., 127
Kato, G., 57
Keith, A., 59
Kennedy, M., 213
Köhler, W., 5, 33, 75-79, 93, 116, 118, 128, 142f., 148, 214, 237f.
König, A., 45
Koffka, K., 66, 76, 78, 90, 92f., 118f., 135, 147, 214
Korte, A., 141, 147
Krause, C. F., 15
Kreezer, G., 59
Kühn, A., 214
Külpe, O., 4-6, 15, 18f., 21, 32, 65f., 115, 122, 127, 143, 216, 237

Laguna, G. A. de, 14
Langfeld, H. S., 16
Lapicque, L., 214
Lashley, K. S., 57, 60, 98, 100-103, 114, 122-124, 158, 191, 193, 213, 235

Lau, E., 118
Lewin, K., 214
Lewis, C. I., 15
Lillie, R. S., 57
Locke, J., 4, 17, 153
Lotze, R. H., 64, 109
Lucas, K., 57
Luce, A., 34

MacDonald, M. K., 35
Mach, E., 15, 34, 127, 160, 182, 237
Martius, G., 120
McDougall, W., 214
McFarland, R. A., 213
Mendeléyev, D. I., 18, 151
Meumann, E., 34, 147, 218
Meyer, M., 59
Mill, James, 17, 197f., 216
Möller, E. F., 118
Moore, R. C., 144, 148
Müller, G. E., 24, 70, 115, 160, 164, 181, 183, 217, 237
Müller, J., 63, 65, 100, 115, 120, 122, 157-160, 171, 173, 182, 185
Myers, C. S., 115

Nafe, J. P., 18, 32, 34, 171f., 176-179, 184f.
Nagel, W., 119
Nagge, J. W., 149
Newton, I., 159
Nicholas, H., 146

Ogden, R. M., 33, 117

Pattie, F. A., 84, 117
Peak, H., 213
Pendleton, C. R., 185
Pillsbury, W. B., 199f., 216
Pintner, R., 212
Poffenberger, A, T., 218
Poppelreuter, W., 120, 214
Pratt, C. C., 126, 183, 236

Quain, R., 186

Rahn, C., 21, 32, 122
Rand, G., 183
Reeves, P., 58
Reimann, E., 119
Révész, G., 33
Rich, G. J., 33, 82, 84, 116
Rivers, W. H. R., 58, 125, 194

Robinson, E. S., 218
Rubin, E., 106, 122

Schäfer, E. A., 186
Schubotz, F., 120
Schumann, F., 183, 217
Schur, E., 96, 119
Shepard, J. F., 237
Sherrington, C. S., 186
Skinner, B. F., 219
Smith, May, 215
Smith, M. K., 217
Soury, J., 122
Spearman, C., 212
Stern, W., 191, 212
Stevens, S. S., 117
Stone, S., 147
Stumpf, C., 18, 32f., 64, 122

Talbot, E. B., 32
Thorndike, E. L., 214
Titchener, E. B., 4f, 15, 18f., 22, 32-34, 66, 78, 82, 88f., 116f., 122, 127f., 146f., 152, 172, 181f., 184, 216f., 222f., 225-227, 236f.
Tolman, E. C., 215, 237
Troland, L. T., 16, 116, 122, 162-164, 166, 179, 182f., 216, 237

Vierordt, K., 127, 146, 148
Volkmann, A. W., 57

Washburn, M. F., 32, 215, 237
Watt, H. J., 117
Weber, E. H., 34, 172, 184
Weld, H. P., 117
Wertheimer, M., 66, 77
Wever, E. G., 50-54, 59, 74, 117, 167
Wiley, L. E., 123
Wilkinson, G., 59
William of Occam, 16
Woodworth, R. S., 15
Wrightson, T., 59
Wundt, W., 4-6, 15, 19, 64, 70, 87, 127, 134, 143, 146f., 166, 183, 216, 226, 237

Yerkes, R. M., 214
Yokoyama, M., 237
Young, T., 159, 182

Zeigarnik, B., 214
Zener, K. E., 117
Zoll, P. M., 84, 117
Zoth, O., 96, 119
Zotterman, Y., 58

INDEX OF SUBJECTS

Absolute judgments, 117
Absolute pitch, 168-170
Accommodation, visual, 87f.
Actuality, conscious, 32
Acuity, visual, physiology of, 45f., 58
Adaptation, as protensitive process, 141
Affectivity, as sensory, 18, 32
    introspection on, 225f., 237
Afferent fibers, 37
After-images, as protensitive events, 141
Alley experiments, 96f., 120f.
All-or-none functions, statistical, 219f.
All-or-none law, neural, 36, 38-41, 57
Amnesia, relation to anesthesia, 224f.
    relation to amnesia, 224f.
Analysis, in science, 8f.
Anesthesia, as unconsciousness, 224
    relation to amnesia, 224f.
Apparent movement, as protensitive event, 141f., 147
Appetite, quality, 26, 34
Associationism, 3, 201
Atomism, temporal, 128f.
Attensity, 19, 23, 32f., 217
Attention, 194-201, 215-217
    as affecting size, 97f., 121
    as cognitive process, 200f., 216f.
    as limitation of consciousness, 235
    as reportability, 200f.
    as sensory clearness, 217
    Cattell's research, 196f., 215f.
    cognitive function, 225
    conditions, 198
    degree, 200f.
    duration, 198-200, 216
    fluctuation, 198-200, 216
    focus and margin, 200, 217

Attention, history of concept, 216f.
    inertia, as protensitive phenomenon, 142, 147f.
    introspection of, 200f.
    Jevons's experiment, 195f., 215
    Pillsbury's experiment, 199, 216
    range, 194-197, 215f.
    range limited, 194, 215f.
    relation to intelligence, 198
    relation to introspection, 226f.
    relation to mass action, 198
    relation to mental organization, 194, 196
    two-level theory, 200f., 217
Attributes, as object of observation, 20f.
    primacy among, 122
    quantitative, 181
    sensation, 19-23, 32f.
    tonal, 33
Auditory localization, see Localization
Auditory quality, see Quality
Auditory theory, 44f., 49-54, 59
    analysis, 165f.
    frequency, 167f., 170, 184
    Helmholtz's, 160f.
    Mach's analysis, 160, 182
    Ohm's law, 167f., 170
    physiology, 170
    resonance, 161, 167, 170
    resonance-frequency, 166f., 170, 183
Axon, 37

Behaviorism, 4, 17
Binocular parallax, 88f.
Body and mind, see Mind and Body
Brain, as integrating organ, 229
    as relational organ, 229-233
    excitatory patterns, 93f., 118f.

Brain, localization of function, *see* Localization of function
organ of consciousness, 5, 229-233
Brightness, cutaneous, 26
tonal, 25
See also Brilliance
Brilliance, visual, 23f.; discrimination, 104f.; physiology of, 45f., 58

Causality, as correlation, 12
concept, 8
continuity, 12, 14
Cause and effect, as relationship of consciousness, 229f.
Cerebral localization of function, *see* Localization of function
Clearness, *see* Attensity
Colligation, 65f.
Color pyramid, 23f., 33
Color theory, 24f., 33, 162-165, 182f.
central factors, 164f., 183
cortical gray, 24f., 160, 164
dependence on discrimination, 160
frequency of light, 183
Helmholtz's, 159
Hering's, 160
Ladd-Franklin's, 183
photochemical reaction, 183
three components, 163
Young-Helmholtz, 160
Common sensibility, pain, 176
Comparison, successive, as protensitive, 142, 148
Concomitant variation, as experimental method, 8f.
Conditioned reflex, 38
Conscious present, 134-136
Consciousness, as cognitive, 234
as defined by anesthesia, 224
as dependent on attention, 231f.
as dependent on learning, 230, 237
as dependent on nervous system, 230
as discrimination, 187, 212, 234
as meaningful, 222f., 236f.
as process, 216
as relational, 222f., 233-237

Consciousness, as sensory, 31f.
differentiation, 234
inconsistencies of traditional view, 232f.
introspective description, 227-229
localization in brain, 231, 234 237
nature, 221-238
process-nature, 227f.
regress of meaning in introspection, 228
relation to amnesia, 224f.
relation to knowledge, 230
relation to sleep, 225, 237
relational theory, 222-233, 236f.
See also Introspection
Constancy hypothesis, afferent, 75f., 99f., 116
psychophysical, 75f., 116
psychophysiological, 75-77, 116
Constructs, in science, 7
Context theory, of meaning, 155f., 182, 222f., 236f.
of perception, 88f., 108f., 114f., 124, 155f., 182
Contour, visual, 106, 122
Convergence, visual, 87f.
Correlation, as experimental method, 8
as identification, 14, 16, 238
psychophysical, 8-14, 16, 74
Correspondence, psychophysiological, 61, 69-77, 115, 232, 237f.; form, 99; Gestalt psychology, 75-77, 93, 116; protensitive, 128, 137f., 144-146
Corresponding points, retinal, 71f., 90
Cortical gray, 24f., 160, 164
Current of action, as protensitive process, 139
Cutaneous limen of duality, 68f., 73, 110, 125
Cutaneous quality, *see* Quality
Cutaneous receptors, 172-174, 176f., 179, 181, 184-186
free endings, 185f.
histological research, 185f.
Cutaneous sensibility, 173-181, 184-186
adaptation, 174

Cutaneous sensibility, afferent excitation, 177f.
  brightness, 177
  Head's theory, 58
  Nafe's theory, 177-179, 184
  pain spots, 175, 184
  pressure spots, 175, 184
  quantitative theory, 177-179, 184
  temperature spots, 173-175, 184
Cutaneous spots, 161, 173-175, 184
Cutaneous summation, 69

Dendrite, 37
Depth, visual, 86-94, 118f.; accommodation, 87f.; binocular parallax, 88f.; convergence, 87f.; glassy sensation, 92, 118; perspective, 92f., 118; relation to form, 86f.; relation to illusions, 91-93, 118; retinal disparity, 88-91, 93, 118f.; secondary criteria, 89, 92f.; solid excitatory fields, 118f.
Dichotic stimulation, 112-114, 125f.
Dimensions, of consciousness, 17-35, 234f.; physiology, 187f., 212; place theories, 187f., 212; present status, 221; problem of primacy, 122
  of physics, 22f.
Discrimination, as function of brain, 229
Disperson, auditory, 44f.
  Bernstein, 68
  retinal, 42f., 57f.
  tactual, 43f., 58
Distance, see Depth
Dizziness, 34
Double-alternation maze, 145, 148f.
Double aspect theory, 4, 16, 238
Double personality, 199
Dualism, 3-8, 12, 14-16, 74, 236
  anesthesia, 224
  Gestalt psychology, 76f.
  See also Parallelism
Duration, see Protensity

Ear, structure of cochlea, 44, 59
Effector, 37
Efferent fiber, 37
Elementarism, 18, 20f., 30, 32

Elements, mental, 18
Empiricism, 3
Epicritic functions, 193f.
Epicritic sensibility, 58, 73, 124f.
Epistemology of reality, 154f.
Equipotentiality, cerebral, 98, 103-105, 123; intelligence, 191; relation to memory, 202
Excitation of nerve, 36-41
Existentiality, of conscious data, 6, 223, 228
Experience, ambiguous concept, 7, 14, 154f.
  dependent, 4-6, 14
  direct, 5-7, 10f., 13f.
  immediate, 4-6, 10f., 13f., 226
  independent, 4-6, 14
  mediate, 4-6, 10f., 14
Experimental method, 8f.
Extension, 78-86
  cerebral, 78f.
  distinguished from form, 78, 80
  Gestalt psychology, 78f.
  relation to size, 94
  smell, 86, 117
  tactual, 79f.
  taste, 85
  visual, 78-80
  See also Extensity, Tonal volume
Extensity, 19f., 23, 62-126
  as dimension, 28-30
  auditory, 165f.
  history of problem, 62-68, 115
  phenomenal, 67
  physiology, 234f.
  relation of place theory of quality, 165
  relation to protensity, 127f., 146
  tactual, 35; visual imagery, 79
  visual, 35
  See also Depth, Form, Localization, perceptual, Size, Space perception

Fact, as correlation, 9, 11
Fechner's law, see Weber-Fechner function
Feeling, as sensation, 18, 32
  introspection on, 225f., 237
Forgetting, as protensitive process, 142

Form, perceived, 99-107, 121f.
  phenomenology, 99
  protensitive, 128
  relation to size, 94
  visual, cerebral localization, 103,
    123; contours, 106, 122
  See also Depth
Form-quality, 99, 121
  extensive, 65
  school, 20
  temporal, 128
Frequency, as protensitive stimulus,
  to intensity, 141; to pitch,
    141
Frequency functions, significance,
  219f.
Frequency theory, of intensity, 46-
  50, 58f.; somesthetic, 46-48
  of pitch, 49-54, 59
Fusion, tonal, 168-170, 183f.; non-
  musical intervals, 183f.

Gemeingefühl, 172, 184
Generalization, in science, 8f.
Geneticism, 115
  protensitive, 127
  visual depth, 87
Gestalt psychology, 7, 21
  as dualistic, 76f.
  extensity, 66
  learning, 201
Gestaltqualität, see Form-quality
Glassy sensation, 92, 118
Gray, cortical, 24f., 160, 164

Heat, quality, 26, 34, 161f., 173, 182
Hunger, quality, 26, 34
Hypotheses, 8, 31, 74
Hysteria, relation to unconscious-
  ness, 225

Idea, concept, 18
Identification, by correlation, 16,
  238
Identity theory, 16, 238
Illusions, moon, 95f., 119f.
  optical relation to visual depth,
    91-93, 118
Image, related to sensation, 18
Immediate experience, 4-6, 10f.,
  13f., 226

Indifference point, time-sense, 135f.,
  148
Induction, experimental, 8f.
Inference, in science, 6f., 10f.
Insight, as motivational, 215
  concept, 214
  rats in maze, 215
  relation to intelligence, 191
  relation to learning, 206, 210-212,
    218f.
Intelligence, 188-194, 212-215
  all-or-none tests, 189f., 213f.
  as aptitude for learning, 190
  as cerebral differentiation, 235
  as common factor, 188
  as correctness, 190
  as dependent on mass action, 103,
    191-194, 214
  as discrimination, 190f., 212-214
  as insight, 191, 214f.
  as speed, 189, 213f.
  concept, 188f., 212f.
  Lashley's experiments, 191-193,
    214
  power tests, 189, 213f.
  relation of time to range, 213
  relation to attention, 198
  relation to brain size, 192, 214
  space theory, 213
  speed tests, 189, 213f.
Intensity, 19f., 23, 36-61
  as central summation, 56f., 60
  as cerebral localization, 55-57, 60
  as dimension, 28
  frequency theory, 46-50, 58f.
  multiple fiber theory, 42-46, 57f.
  physiology of, 36, 42-61, 234
  sensory, 55-57, 60
  visual, 23-25, 33
  volley theory, 50-55, 59
Interactionism, 4, 12, 16
Interval, musical, 168-170, 183f.
Introspection, as altering mind, 226
  as behavioral, 226
  as cognitive, 227
  as context, 226, 228
  as immediate experience, 226
  as inferential, 236
  as interpretative, 10f., 13f.
  as method, 15
  as retrospection, 228

Introspection, by animals, 227
  dependence on report, 227
  of duration, 129
  of feeling, 225f., 237
  of introspection, 200, 227-229,
    237
  physiology of, 56f., 100, 105, 180,
    212
  regress of meaning, 228
  Titchener's formula, 226f.
Introspectionism, 4-6, 17, 31
Irradiation, *see* Dispersion
Isomorphism, *see* Correspondence,
  psychophysiological

Kinesthesis, *see* Quality, somesthetic
Knowledge, relation to consciousness, 230
  relation to learning, 230
Korte's laws, 141, 147

Latent time, sensory, 147
Learning, 201-212, 217-220
  active participation as aid, 206,
    215
  as all-or-none process, 211f., 218-
    220
  as dependent on principles of
    probability, 210, 219f.
  as discrimination, 201
  as function of difficulty of mate-
    rial, 209
  diminishing returns of repetitions,
    209f., 218
  direct interference, 206f.
  facilitation, 202-206, 211
  frequency functions as measures,
    219f.
  instantaneous with insight, 191f.,
    214
  interference, 206-211, 218; in large
    organizations, 208f., 218
  law of frequency, 235f.
  meaningfulness as aid, 204-206,
    218
  mechanical not effective, 206, 215
  mnemotechnical aids, 205
  nonsense, 204f., 218
  organization as aid, 202f., 218
  purposeful, 206, 215
  relation to attention, 201

Learning, relation to insight, 206,
  218f.
  relation to intelligence, 201
  relation to mass action, 209-212
  relation to mental organization,
    201
  relation to range of atttention,
    210-212
  relation to range of consciousness,
    235f.
  retention during sleep, 208, 218
  retroactive inhibition, 207f.
  rhythm as aid, 202f., 217f.
  sense, 204-206, 218
  spatial localization as aid, 205
  statistical artifacts in curve, 220
  transfer, of organization, 203,
    218; positive and negative,
    206f.
  trial-and-error, 191f.
Local signs, 64, 66, 109f.
Localization, auditory, 73, 112-114,
  125, 170; conditions, 112f.,
  125f.; for different frequencies,
  126; physiology of, 113f., 125f.;
  reduction to intensitive difference, 113; reduction to time
  difference, 113, 125
  perceptual, as associative, 66; as
  relativistic, 107-109, 114f.; of
  objects, 104f.; physiology of,
  114f.; relation to form, 107;
  significance of nerve-division,
  110f., 124f.; surrogation, 79,
  81, 107f., 124; visual imagery
  as surrogate, 107f., 124
  tactual, 72, 110f., 124f.
  visual, 71f.
Localization of function, cerebral,
  77-79, 100-107, 122, 231, 237;
  Fortuyn's areas, 101f., 122f.;
  fragility, 123; Franz's research,
  123; heirarchy, 104f., 123; Hunter's criticism, 124; Lashley's
  research, 102-105, 122-124;
  modality, 157f.
  consciousness in brain, 231, 237

Mass action, 98, 103-105, 123f.
  as basis for intelligence, 191-194,
    214

Mass action, differentiation of excitatory pattern, 192-194, 214
relation to attention, 198, 235
relation to intelligence, 235
relation to learning, 209-212
Meaning, as datum of introspection, 227
as relation, 222f., 236f.
as response, 222f., 237
context theory, 222f., 236f.
perception, 151-153, 182
relation to consciousness, 222f., 236f.
relation to stimulus and response, 153, 182
Measurement, psychophysical, 10-12
Membrane theory of nerve conduction, 40f., 57
Memory, as persistence of organization, 201f.
relation to equipotentiality, 202
See also Learning
Mental chemistry, 18
Method, experimental, 8f.
Mind and body, double aspect theory, 4, 16, 238
identity theory, 16, 238
interactionism, 4, 12, 16
problem, 3-16
psychophysical parallelism, 4, 13f., 16f., 70, 137f., 144-146, 180, 224, 232f.
Modality, as fundamental in psychology, 152f.
as quality, 27f.
as relativistic, 156f.
cerebral localization, 157
cognitive differentiation, 158
comparison across, 182
cutaneous, 171-181, 184-186
discrimination, 155f.
Helmholtz's use of term, 172
immediate in introspection, 154
physiology, 157f., 182, 235
qualitative signs, 156
variation with fixed meaning, 151-153, 182
See also Quality
Monism, in relation to psychology, 4, 15f., 17
Moon illusion, 95f., 119f.

Multiple fiber theory, Hecht's evidence, 45f., 58
of intensity, 42-46, 57f.
Muscle sense, 18
Muscular reaction, 143, 148
Musical interval, perception, 168-170, 183f.

Nativism, extensive, 78, 115
protensive, 127
Nerve conduction, 40f., 57
Nerve excitation, 36-41
Nerve impulse, 38-41
Nervous system, as integrator, 37, 229
See also Brain, Localization of function
Neuron, 37
Noise, 25

Objects, perceived, stability, 121
Observation, as altering the existential, 223, 226 ,
as inferential, 31, 236
direct, 10f., 30
immediate, meaning of concept, 136f.
of feeling, 225f., 237
of protensity, 128f.
protensive, 137
relation to inference, 236
Octave, perception of, 168-170
Organic qualities, 25f., 33f., 171-181, 184f.
Organization, as problem of psychology, 187f.
levels within psychology, 188
of consciousness, 7, 234f.; relation to reduction, 236

Pain, as common sensibility, 176, 180f., 186
as intense sensation, 180
as summation, 176, 180f., 185
spots, 175
Paradoxical cold, 173
Parallelism, psychophysical, 4, 13f., 16f., 70, 232f.; as explaining anesthesia, 224; cutaneous sensibility, 180; for protensity, 137f., 144-146

Parsimony, principle of, 16, 38
Perception, of objects, 104f., 121
Phenomenology, 5, 21f., 30
  Hering's, 65
  method, 226
  of form, 99
  of protension, 133-137, 146
Phi-phenomenon, as protensitive event, 141f., 147
Physical science, 4-8
  dimensions of, 22f.
Pitch, terms 'high' and 'low', 126
Place theory, of conscious dimensions, 234
  of consciousness, 187f., 212
Prior entry, as protensitive phenomenon, 142, 147f.
Projection theory, Bernstein's, 67-70, 73f., 115f.
  extensity, 62f., 67-74, 115f.
  Gestalt psychology, 93
  of form, 99, 106
Protension, 133-137, 146f.
  conscious present, 134-136
  immediately perceived, 133-137, 146
Protensity, 19f., 23, 30
  attribute of duration, 127
  bodily cues, 131
  concept, 127, 146
  estimation of duration, 135f., 147
  estimation of time after sleep, 130f., 146
  indifference point, 135f., 147
  integration, 133-138, 146f.; in successive comparison, 142, 148; in temporal maze, 149
  intensitive surrogation, 143-146, 148
  judgments by rats, 145, 148f.
  judgments, of long times, 130-132; of short times, 132f.
  observation of, 35, 128f., 144-146
  physiological processes, 139-141, 147
  physiology of, 235
  psychophysiological correspondence, 128
  range of consciousness, 134f., 146f.
  relation to extensity, 127f., 146
  relation to mental flux, 129

Protensity, rhythm, 134f., 146f.
  secondary criteria, 131f.
  sensation of time, 127f.
  sensory processes, 141-143
  surrogation, in temporal maze, 149
  temporal processes, 137-146, 147-149
Protopathic sensibility, 58, 73, 111, 124f.
Psychophysical correlation, see Correlation
Psychophysical parallelism, see Parallelism
Psychophysics, 4
  absolute judgments, 117
  frequency functions, 219f.
  inner, 12

Quality, 19f., 23-31, 150-186
  analysis in hearing, 165f.
  analytical theories of color, 159f.
  auditory, 25, 165-170, 183f.
  brightness, cutaneous, 177
  concept, 150f., 181
  cutaneous, 25f., 34, 171-181, 184f.
  differentiated by variation, 156f.
  Helmholtz's visual theory, 159
  in chemistry, 151
  in modality, 27f.
  in physics, 22
  place theory, 158f.; auditory, 166; cutaneous, 178; visual, 164f.
  primacy among dimensions, 106f., 122
  reduction to quantity, 150f., 181
  smell, 26-29, 162
  somesthetic, 25f., 33f., 171-181, 184f.
  specific nerve energy, 158, 182
  taste, 26f., 162
  theories of, 235
  visual, 23-25, 33
  Young's analysis, 159
  See also Auditory theory, Color theory, Cutaneous sensibility, Modality, Specific nerve energy
Quantity, concept, relation to quality, 150f., 181

Range of consciousness, 134f., 146f.
Reaction time, as protensitive process, 142f., 148
Reality, as a construct, 154f.
  concept, 154f.
  psychic, 32
  scientific, 6-8
Receptor, 37
Reduction of conscious content, 195, 197f., 236
  by surrogation, 236
  in learning, 205, 210f.
Reflex, 38
  conditioned, 38
Reflex arc, 37f.
Refractory period, 38-41
Relational theory of consciousness, see Consciousness
Relativism, of perceived size, 94f., 97, 120f.
Response, as any neural effect, 229f.
Retinal disparity, 88-91, 93, 118f.
Reversible perspective, 92f., 118
Rhythm, as protensitive integration, 134f., 146f.
  as protensitive process, 143

Science, classification, 3-6
  realities in, 7
  speculation in, 8
Scopolamine syndrome, 224
Sensation, as construct, 21
  attributes, see Attributes
  concept, 13, 17-22, 32f.
  muscle sense, 18
Sensorial reaction, 143, 148
Size, perceived, 94-98, 119-121; absolute, 95-98; alley experiments, 96f., 120f.; physiology, 95, 98; relation to attention, 97f., 121; relation to distance, 96f., 119-121; relation to extension, 94; relation to form, 94; relation to posture, 95f., 119f.; relation to stability of objects, 121; relativism of, 94f., 97, 120f.
Sleep, as aid to memory, 208, 218
  as concentrated attention, 157, 225, 237
  estimation of time, 131f., 146
  voluntary waking, 132, 146

Smell, extensity, 86, 117
  quality, see Quality
Smell prism, 26-29, 35
Solidity, see Depth
Space, auditory, see Tonal volume
  olfactory, 30
Space perception, geneticism, 64, 67, 78
  history, 62-68, 115
  nativism, 64f., 67
  See also Extension, Extensity, Form, Localization, perceptual, Size
Specific nerve energy, 115, 171f., 184
  as cortical localization, 185
  as projection theory, 62f., 65
  as theory of centers, 158, 182
  audition, 166
  auditory theory, 160f., 182
  color theory, 159f., 182
  Helmholtz's extension, 159, 182
  localization of cerebral function, 157f.
  relation to size, 120
  tactual theory, 161f., 182
Specious present, 134
Speculation, 31, 74
  in science, 8
Stereoscopy, 88-91, 93, 118f.
Stimulus, as any neural cause, 229f.
Subtractive procedure, 143, 148
Successive comparison, as protensitive, 142, 148
Successive induction, 140
Summary of this book, 233-236
Summation, cutaneous, 58
  pain, 176
  physiological, 140, 147
Surrogation, in localization, 79, 81, 107f., 124
Symbolism, in higher mental processes, 197f.
Synapse, 37
  latent time, 140f.

Tactual localization, see Localization
Tactual quality, see Quality
Tactual two-point limen, see Two-point limen
Taste, extensity, 85
  quality, see Quality

Taste tetrahedron, 26f., 35
Temporal maze, 145, 148f.
Thirst, quality, 26, 34
Thought, as symbolic function, 197f.
Time, *see* Protension, Protensity
Time-error, 142, 144, 148
  for judgment of time, 144, 148
Time-sense, 146
  indifference point, 135f.
Tonal volume, 29f., 78, 80-85, 116f.
  as associative, 80f.
  as attribute, 82, 116
  as function of frequency, 82, 84,
    116f.
  as function of intensity, 83f., 116f.
  as unformed, 87
  as visual imagery, 81, 117
  criticism, 117
  dependence on absolute judg-
    ments, 117
  experimental measurement, 82-85,
    116f.
  limens, 82-85, 116f.
  physiology of, 85, 167, 170, 184
  relation to auditory localization,
    116f.
  relation to brightness, 85, 117
Tonality, physiology of, 168-170
Touch blends, 25f.
Touch pyramid, 34

Twilight sleep, 224
Two-point limen, 68f., 73, 110,
  125

Unconscious inference, 154
Unconscious mind, 7

Visual imagery, as localizing surro-
  gate, 79, 81
Visual localization, *see* Localization
Visual perception, *see* Depth, Exten-
  sion, Extensity, Quality
Visual quality, *see* Quality
Vocality, of tones, 25
Volley theory of intensity, 50-55,
  59
  Wever-Bray effect, 50-52, 59
Volume, *see* Extension, Extensity,
  Tonal volume

Weber-Fechner function, 10-13, 60f.
  as ogive, 60f.
  parallelism, 70f.
  physiology, 70f., 115
  psychophysiological correspond-
    ence, 61
Weber's law, *see* Weber-Fechner
  function
Wever-Bray effect, 50-52, 59, 74,
  167